A Historical Introduction to the
Philosophy of Science

JOHN LOSEE

A Historical Introduction to the Philosophy of Science

OXFORD UNIVERSITY PRESS
London   Oxford   New York
1972

Oxford University Press

GLASGOW   NEW YORK   TORONTO   MELBOURNE   WELLINGTON
CAPE TOWN   IBADAN   NAIROBI   DAR ES SALAAM   LUSAKA   ADDIS ABABA
DELHI   BOMBAY   CALCUTTA   MADRAS   KARACHI   LAHORE   DACCA
KUALA LUMPUR   SINGAPORE   HONG KONG   TOKYO

PRINTED IN GREAT BRITAIN
·BY BUTLER & TANNER LTD
FROME AND LONDON

Preface

This book is a historical sketch of the development of views about scientific method. Its emphasis is on developments prior to 1940. No attempt has been made to reproduce the contemporary spectrum of positions on the philosophy of science. My purpose has been exposition rather than criticism, and I have endeavoured to abstain from passing judgement on the achievements of the great philosophers of science.

It is my hope that this book may be of interest both to students of the philosophy of science and to students of the history of science. If, on reading this book, a few such students are encouraged to consult some of the works listed in the Bibliography at the end of the book, I shall consider my effort to have been well spent.

I have received numerous helpful suggestions from Gerd Buchdahl, George Clark, and Rom Harré in the preparation of this volume. I am most grateful, both for their encouragement, and for their criticism. Of course, responsibility for what has emerged is mine alone.

LAFAYETTE COLLEGE
July 1971

Contents

ERRATA

p. 162, quotation l. 3: *for* 'what often has' *read* 'what has often'

p. 183, l. 9: *for* 'which are' *read* 'which are not'

p. 208, l. 19: *for* 'P. A. Schilp' *read* 'P. A. Schilpp'

p. 216: *under entry for* 'Boyle's Law' *insert page reference* '127,'

p. 218: *under entry for* 'Phenomenal realm' *insert page references* ', 58–9'

Introduction

A decision on the scope of the philosophy of science is a pre-condition for writing about its history. Unfortunately, philosophers and scientists are not in accord on the nature of the philosophy of science. Even practising philosophers of science often disagree about the proper subject-matter of their discipline. An example of this lack of agreement is the recent exchange between Stephen Toulmin and Ernest Nagel on whether philosophy of science should be a study of scientific achievement *in vivo*, or a study of problems of explanation and confirmation as reformulated in the terms of deductive logic.[1] To establish a basis for the subsequent historical survey, it will be helpful to sketch four viewpoints on the philosophy of science

One view is that the philosophy of science is the formulation of world-views that are consistent with, and in some sense based on, important scientific theories. On this view, it is the task of the philosopher of science to elaborate the broader implications of science. This may take the form of speculation about ontological categories to be used in speaking about "being-as-such". Thus Alfred North Whitehead urged that recent developments in physics require that the categories 'substance' and 'attribute' be replaced by the categories 'process' and 'influence'.[2] Or it may take the form of pronouncements about the implications of scientific theories for the evaluation of human behaviour, as in Social Darwinism and the theory of ethical relativity. The present study is not concerned with "philosophy of science" in this sense.

A second view is that the philosophy of science is an exposition of the presuppositions and predispositions of scientists. The philosopher of science may point out that scientists presuppose that nature is not capricious, and that there exist in nature regularities of sufficiently low complexity to be accessible to the investigator. In addition, he may uncover the preferences of scientists for deterministic rather than statistical laws, or for mechanistic rather than teleological explanations. This view tends to assimilate philosophy of science to sociology.

A third view is that the philosophy of science is a discipline in which the concepts and theories of the sciences are analysed and clarified. This is not a matter of giving a semi-popular exposition of the latest theories. It is, rather, a matter of becoming clear about the meaning of such terms as 'particle', 'wave', 'potential', and 'complex' in their scientific usage.

But as Gilbert Ryle has pointed out, there is something pretentious about this view of the philosophy of science—as if the scientist needed the philosopher of science to explain to him the meanings of scientific concepts.[3] There would seem to be two possibilities. Either the scientist does understand a concept that he uses, in which case no clarification is required. Or he does not, in which case he must inquire into the relations of that concept to other concepts and to operations of measurement. Such an inquiry is a typical scientific activity. No one would claim that each time a scientist conducts such an inquiry he is practising philosophy of science. At the very least, we must conclude that not every analysis of scientific concepts qualifies as philosophy of science. And yet it may be that certain types of conceptual analysis should be classified as part of the philosophy of science. This question will be left open, pending consideration of a fourth view of the philosophy of science.

A fourth view, which is the view adopted in this work, is that philosophy of science is a second-order criteriology. The philosopher of science seeks answers to such questions as:

(1) What characteristics distinguish scientific inquiry from other types of investigation?

(2) What procedures should scientists follow in investigating nature?

(3) What conditions must be satisfied for a scientific explanation to be correct?

(4) What is the cognitive status of scientific laws and principles?

To ask these questions is to assume a vantage-point one step removed from the practice of science itself. There is a distinction to be made between doing science and thinking about how science ought to be done. The analysis of scientific method is a second-order discipline, the subject-matter of which is the procedures and structures of the various sciences, viz.:

LEVEL	DISCIPLINE	SUBJECT-MATTER
2	Philosophy of Science	Analysis of the Procedures and Logic of Scientific Explanation
1	Science	Explanation of Facts
0		Facts

The fourth view of the philosophy of science incorporates certain aspects of the second and third views. For instance, inquiry into the predispositions of scientists may be relevant to the problem of evaluating scientific theories. This is particularly true for judgements about the completeness of explanations. Einstein, for example, insisted that statistical accounts of radioactive decay were incomplete. He maintained that a complete interpretation would enable predictions to be made of the behaviour of individual atoms.

In addition, analyses of the meanings of concepts may be relevant to the demarcation of scientific inquiry from other types of investigation. For instance, if it can be shown that a term is used in such a way that no means are provided to distinguish its correct application from incorrect application, then interpretations in which the concept is embedded may be excluded from the domain of science. Something like this took place in the case of the concept 'absolute simultaneity'.

The distinction which has been indicated between science and philosophy of science is not a sharp one. It is based on a difference of intent rather than a difference in subject-matter. Consider the question of the relative adequacy of Young's wave theory of light and Maxwell's electromagnetic theory. It is the scientist *qua* scientist who judges Maxwell's theory to be superior. And it is the philosopher of science (or the scientist *qua* philosopher of science) who investigates the general criteria of acceptability that are implied in judgements of this type. Clearly these activities interpenetrate. The scientist who is ignorant of precedents in the evaluation of theories is not likely to do an adequate job of evaluation himself. And the philosopher of science who is ignorant of scientific practice is not likely to make perceptive pronouncements on scientific method.

Recognition that the boundary-line between science and philosophy of science is not sharp is reflected in the choice of subject-matter for this historical survey. The primary source is what scientists and philosophers have said about scientific method. In some cases this is sufficient. It is possible to discuss the philosophies of science of Whewell and Mill, for example, exclusively in terms of what they have written about scientific method. In other cases, however, this is not sufficient. To present the philosophies of science of Galileo and Newton, it is necessary to strike a balance between what they have written about scientific method and their actual scientific practice.

Moreover, developments in science proper, especially the introduction of new types of interpretation, subsequently may provide grist for the mill of philosophers of science. It is for this reason that brief accounts have been included of the work of Euclid, Archimedes, and the classical atomists, among others.

REFERENCES

1 Stephen Toulmin, *Sci. Am.* 214, no. 2 (Feb. 1966), 129–33; 214, no. 4 (Apr. 1966), 9–11;
Ernest Nagel, *Sci. Am.* 214, no. 4 (Apr. 1966), 8–9.
2 Whitehead himself did not use the term 'influence'. For his position on the relation of science and philosophy see, for example, his *Modes of Thought* (Cambridge: Cambridge University Press, 1938), 173–232.
3 Gilbert Ryle, 'Systematically Misleading Expressions', in A. Flew, ed., *Essays on Logic and Language—First Series* (Oxford: Blackwell, 1951), 11–13.

1
Aristotle's Philosophy of Science

ARISTOTLE (384–322 B.C.) was born in Stagira in northern Greece. His father was physician to the Macedonian court. At the age of seventeen Aristotle was sent to Athens to study at Plato's Academy. He was associated with the Academy for a period of twenty years. Upon Plato's death in 347 B.C., and the subsequent election of the mathematically-oriented Speucippus to head the Academy, Aristotle chose to pursue his biological and philosophical studies in Asia Minor. In 342 B.C. he returned to Macedonia as tutor to Alexander the Great, a relationship which lasted two or three years.

By 335 B.C. Aristotle had returned to Athens and had established the Peripatetic School in the Lyceum. In the course of his teaching at the Lyceum, he discussed logic, epistemology, physics, biology, ethics, politics, and aesthetics. The works that have come to us from this period appear to be compilations of lecture notes rather than polished pieces intended for publication. They range from speculation about the attributes predicable of 'being-as-such' to encyclopedic presentations of data on natural history and the constitutions of Greek city-states. The *Posterior Analytics* is Aristotle's principal work on the philosophy of science. In addition, the *Physics* and the *Metaphysics* contain discussions of certain aspects of scientific method.

Aristotle left Athens after the death of Alexander in 323 B.C., lest Athens "sin twice against philosophy". He died the following year.

ARISTOTLE was the first philosopher of science. He created the discipline by analysing certain problems that arise in connection with scientific explanation.

ARISTOTLE'S INDUCTIVE–DEDUCTIVE METHOD

Aristotle viewed scientific inquiry as a progression from observations to general principles and back to observations. He maintained that the scientist should induce explanatory principles from the phenomena to be explained, and then deduce statements about the phenomena from premises which include these principles. Aristotle's inductive–deductive procedure may be represented as follows:

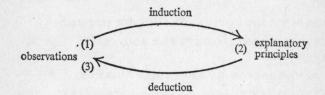

Aristotle believed that scientific inquiry begins with knowledge that certain events occur, or that certain properties coexist. Scientific explanation is achieved only when statements about these events or properties are deduced from explanatory principles. Scientific explanation thus is a transition from knowledge of a fact (point (1) in the diagram above) to knowledge of the reasons for the fact (point (3)).

For instance, a scientist might apply the inductive–deductive procedure to a lunar eclipse in the following way. He begins with observation of the progressive darkening of the lunar surface. He then induces from this observation, and other observations, several general principles: that light travels in straight lines, that opaque bodies cast shadows, and that a particular configuration of two opaque bodies near a luminous body places one opaque body in the shadow of the other. From these general principles, and the condition that the earth and moon are opaque bodies, which, in this instance, have the required geometrical relationship to the luminous sun, he then deduces a statement about the lunar eclipse. He has progressed from factual knowledge that the moon's surface has darkened to an understanding of why this took place.

The Inductive Stage

According to Aristotle, every particular thing is a union of matter and form. Matter is what makes the particular a unique individual, and form is what makes the particular a member of a class of similar things. To specify the form of a particular is to specify the properties it shares with other particulars. For example, the form of a particular giraffe includes the property of having a four-chambered stomach.

Aristotle maintained that it is by induction that generalizations about forms are drawn from sense experience. He discussed two types of induction. The two types share the characteristic of proceeding from particular statements to general statements.

The first type of induction is simple enumeration, in which statements about individual objects or events are taken as the basis for a generalization about a species of which they are members. Or, at a higher level, statements about individual species are taken as a basis for a generalization about a genus.

Aristotle's First Type of Induction:
Simple Enumeration

Premisses		Conclusion
what is observed to be true of several individuals	generalization ⟶	what is presumed to be true of the species to which the individuals belong
what is observed to be true of several species	generalization ⟶	what is presumed to be true of the genus to which the species belong

In an inductive argument by simple enumeration, the premisses and conclusion contain the same descriptive terms. A typical argument by simple enumeration has the form:

$$a_1 \text{ has property } P$$
$$a_2 \quad '' \quad '' \quad P$$
$$a_3 \quad '' \quad '' \quad P$$
$$\therefore \text{ All } a\text{'s have property } P.$$

The second type of induction is a direct intuition of those general principles which are exemplified in phenomena. Intuitive induction is a matter of insight. It is an ability to see that which is "essential" in the data of sense experience. An example given by Aristotle is the case of a scientist who notices on several occasions that the bright side of the moon is turned toward the sun, and who concludes that the moon shines by reflected sunlight.[1]

The operation of intuitive induction is analogous to the operation of the "vision" of the taxonomist. The taxonomist is a scientist who has learned to "see" the generic attributes and *differentiae* of a specimen. There is a sense in which the taxonomist "sees more than" the untrained observer of the same specimen. The taxonomist knows what to look for. This is an ability which is achieved, if at all, only after extensive experience. It is probable that when Aristotle wrote about intuitive induction, this is the sort of "vision" he had in mind. Aristotle himself was a highly successful taxonomist who undertook to classify some 540 biological species.

The Deductive Stage

In the second stage of scientific inquiry, the generalizations reached by induction are used as premisses for the deduction of statements about the initial observations. Aristotle placed an important restriction on the kinds of statements that can occur as premisses and conclusions of deductive arguments in science. He allowed only those statements which assert that one class is included within, or is excluded from, a second class. If 'S' and 'P' are selected to stand for the two classes, the statements that Aristotle allowed are:

Type	Statement	Relation
A	All S are P	S wholly included in P
E	No S are P	S wholly excluded from P
I	Some S are P	S partially included in P
O	Some S are not P	S partially excluded from P

Aristotle held that type *A* is the most important of these four types. He believed that certain properties inhere essentially in the individuals of certain classes, and that statements of the form 'All *S* are *P*' reproduce the structure of these relations. Perhaps for this reason, Aristotle maintained that a proper scientific explanation should be given in terms of statements of this type. More specifically, he cited the syllogism in Barbara as the paradigm of scientific demonstration. This syllogism consists of *A*-type statements arranged in the following way:

$$\frac{\text{All } M \text{ are } P.}{\text{All } S \text{ are } M.}$$
$$\therefore \text{All } S \text{ are } P.$$

where *P*, *S*, and *M* are the major, minor, and middle terms of the syllogism.

Aristotle showed that this type of syllogism is valid. If it is true that every *S* is included in *M* and every *M* is included in *P*, it also must be true that every *S* is included in *P*. This is the case regardless of what classes are designated by '*S*', '*P*', and '*M*'. One of Aristotle's great achievements was to insist that the validity of an argument is determined solely by the *relationship* between premisses and conclusion.

Aristotle construed the deductive stage of scientific inquiry as the interposition of middle terms between the subject and predicate terms of the statement to be proved. For example, the statement 'All planets are bodies that shine steadily' may be deduced by selecting 'bodies near the earth' as middle term. In syllogistic form the proof is:

> All bodies near the earth are bodies that shine steadily.
> All planets are bodies near the earth.
> ∴ All planets are bodies that shine steadily.

Upon application of the deductive stage of scientific procedure, the scientist has advanced from knowledge of a fact about the planets to an understanding of why this fact is as it is.[2]

EMPIRICAL REQUIREMENTS FOR SCIENTIFIC EXPLANATION

Aristotle recognized that a statement which predicates an attribute of a class term always can be deduced from more than one set of premisses. Different arguments result when different middle terms are selected, and some arguments are more satisfactory than others. The previously given syllogism, for instance, is more satisfactory than the following:

> All stars are bodies that shine steadily.
> All planets are stars.
> ∴ All planets are bodies that shine steadily.

Both syllogisms have the same conclusion and the same logical form, but the syllogism immediately above has false premisses. Aristotle insisted that the premisses of a satisfactory explanation must be true. He thereby excluded from the class of satisfactory explanations those valid syllogisms that have true conclusions but false premisses.

The requirement that the premisses be true is one of four extra-logical requirements which Aristotle placed on the premisses of scientific explanations. The other three requirements are that the premisses must be indemonstrable, better known than the conclusion, and causes of the attribution made in the conclusion.[3]

Although Aristotle did state that the premisses of every adequate scientific explanation ought to be indemonstrable, it is clear from the context of his presentation that he was concerned to insist only that there must be *some* principles within each science that cannot be deduced from more basic principles. The existence of some indemonstrable principles within a science is necessary in order to avoid an infinite regress in explanations. Consequently, not all knowledge within a science is susceptible to proof. Aristotle held that the most general laws of a science, and the definitions which stipulate the meanings of the attributes proper to that science, are indemonstrable.

The requirement that the premisses be "better known than" the conclusion reflects Aristotle's belief that the general laws of a science ought to be self-evident. Aristotle knew that a deductive argument can convey no more information than is implied by its premisses, and he insisted that the first principles of demonstration be at least as evident as the conclusions drawn from them.

The most important of the four requirements is that of causal relatedness. It is possible to construct valid syllogisms with true premisses in such a way that the premisses fail to state the cause of the attribution which is made in the conclusion. It is instructive to compare the following two syllogisms about ruminants, or cud-chewing animals:

Syllogism of the Reasoned Fact

All ruminants with four-chambered stomachs are animals with missing upper incisor teeth.
All oxen are ruminants with four-chambered stomachs.

∴ All oxen are animals with missing upper incisor teeth.

Syllogism of the Fact

All ruminants with cloven hoofs are animals with missing upper incisor teeth.
All oxen are ruminants with cloven hoofs.

∴ All oxen are animals with missing upper incisor teeth.

Aristotle would say that the premisses of the above syllogism of the reasoned fact state the cause of the fact that oxen have missing incisors in the upper jaw. The ability of ruminants to store partially chewed food in one stomach chamber and to return it to the mouth for further mastication explains why they do not need, and do not have, incisors in the upper jaw. By contrast, the premisses of the corresponding syllogism of the fact do not state the cause of the missing upper incisors. Aristotle would say that the correlation of hoof structure and jaw structure is an accidental one.

What is needed at this point is a criterion to distinguish causal from accidental correlations. Aristotle recognized this need. He suggested that in a causal relation the attribute (1) is true of every instance of the subject, (2) is true of the subject precisely and not as part of a larger whole, and (3) is "essential to" the subject.

Aristotle's criteria of causal relatedness leave much to be desired. The first criterion may be applied to eliminate from the class of causal relations any relation to which there are exceptions. But one could establish a causal relation by applying this criterion only for those cases in which the subject class can be enumerated completely. However, the great majority of causal relations of interest to the scientist have an open scope of predication. For example, that objects more dense than water sink in water is a relation which is believed to hold for all objects, past, present, and future, and not just for those few objects that have been placed in water. It is not possible to show that every instance of the subject class has this property.

Aristotle's third criterion identifies causal relation and the "essential" attribution of a predicate to a subject. This pushes back the problem one stage. Unfortunately, Aristotle failed to provide a criterion to determine which attributions are "essential". To be sure, he did suggest that 'animal' is an essential predicate of 'man', and 'musical' is not, and that slitting an animal's throat is essentially related to its death, whereas taking a stroll is not essentially related to the occurrence of lightning.[4] But it is one thing to give examples of essential predication and accidental predication, and another thing to stipulate a general criterion for making the distinction.

The Structure of a Science

Although Aristotle did not specify a criterion of the "essential" attribution of a predicate to a subject class, he did insist that each particular science has a distinctive subject genus and set of predicates. The subject genus of physics, for example, is the class of cases in which bodies change their locations in space. Among the predicates which are proper to this science are 'position', 'speed', and 'resistance'. Aristotle emphasized that a satisfactory explanation of a phenomenon must utilize the predicates of that science to which the phenomenon belongs. It would be inappropriate, for instance, to explain the motion of a projectile in terms of such distinctively biological predicates as 'growth' and 'development'.

Aristotle held that an individual science is a deductively organized group of statements. At the highest level of generality are the first principles of *all* demonstration—the Principles of Identity, Non-contradiction, and the Excluded Middle. These are principles applicable to *all* deductive arguments. At the next highest level of generality are the first principles and definitions of the particular science. The first principles of physics, for example, would include:

All motion is either natural or violent.
All natural motion is motion toward a natural place.
    e.g. solid objects move by nature toward the centre of the earth.
Violent motion is caused by the continuing action of an agent. (Action-at-a-distance is impossible.)
A vacuum is impossible.

The first principles of a science are not subject to deduction from more basic principles. They are the most general true statements that can be made about the predicates proper to the science. As such, the first principles are the starting-points of all demonstration within the science. They function as premises for the deduction of those correlations which are found at lower levels of generality.

The Four Causes

Aristotle did place one additional requirement on scientific interpretations. He demanded that an adequate explanation of a correlation or process should specify all four aspects of causation. The four aspects are the formal cause, the material cause, the efficient cause, and the final cause.

A process susceptible to this kind of analysis is the skin-colour change of a chameleon as it moves from a bright-green leaf to a dull-grey twig. The formal cause is the pattern of the process. To describe the formal cause is to specify a generalization about the conditions under which this kind of colour change takes place. The material cause is that substance in the skin which undergoes a change of colour. The efficient cause is the transition from leaf to twig, a transition accompanied by a change in reflected light and a corresponding chemical change in the skin of the chameleon. The final cause of the process is that the chameleon should escape detection by its predators.

Aristotle insisted that every scientific explanation of a correlation or process should include an account of its final cause, or *telos*. Teleological explanations are explanations which use the expression 'in order that', or its equivalent. Aristotle required teleological explanations not only of the growth and development of living organisms, but also of the motions of inanimate objects. For example, he held that fire rises in order to reach its "natural place" (a spherical shell just inside the orbit of the moon).

Teleological interpretations need not presuppose conscious deliberation and choice. To say, for instance, that 'chameleons change colour in order to escape detection' is not to claim a conscious activity on the part of chameleons. Nor is it to claim that the behaviour of chameleons implements some "cosmic purpose".

However, teleological interpretations do presuppose that a future state of affairs determines the way in which a present state of affairs unfolds. An acorn develops in the way it does in order that it should realize its natural end as an oak-tree; a stone falls in order that it should achieve its natural end—a state of rest as near as possible to the centre of the earth; and so on. In each case, the future state "pulls along", as it were, the succession of states which leads up to it.

Aristotle criticized philosophers who sought to explain change exclusively in terms of material causes and efficient causes. He was particularly critical of the atomism of Democritus and Leucippus, in which natural processes were "explained" by the aggregation and scattering of invisible atoms. To a great extent, Aristotle's criticism was based on the atomists' neglect of final causes.

Aristotle also criticized those Pythagorean natural philosophers who believed that they had explained a process when they had found a mathematical relationship exemplified in it. According to Aristotle, the Pythagorean approach suffers from exclusive preoccupation with formal causes.

It should be added, however, that Aristotle did recognize the importance of numerical relations and geometrical relations within the science of physics. Indeed, he singled out a group of "composite sciences"—astronomy, optics, harmonics, and mechanics*—whose subject-matter is mathematical relationships among physical objects.

THE DEMARCATION OF EMPIRICAL SCIENCE

Aristotle sought, not only to mark off the subject matter of each individual science, but also to distinguish empirical science, as a whole, from pure mathematics. He achieved this demarcation by distinguishing between applied mathematics, as practised in the composite sciences, and pure mathematics, which deals with number and figure in the abstract.

Aristotle maintained that, whereas the subject-matter of empirical science is change, the subject-matter of pure mathematics is that which is unchanging. The pure mathematician abstracts from physical situations certain quantitative aspects of bodies and their relations, and deals exclusively with these aspects. Aristotle held that these mathematical forms have no objective existence. Only in the mind of the mathematician do the forms survive the destruction of the bodies from which they are abstracted.

THE NECESSARY STATUS OF FIRST PRINCIPLES

Aristotle claimed that genuine scientific knowledge has the status of necessary truth. He maintained that the properly formulated first principles of the sciences, and their deductive consequences, could not be other than true. Since first principles predicate attributes of class terms, Aristotle would seem to be committed to the following theses:

(1) Certain properties inhere essentially in the individuals of certain classes; an individual would not be a member of one of these classes if it did not possess the properties in question.

(2) An identity of structure exists in such cases between the universal affirmative statement which predicates an attribute of a class term, and the non-verbal inherence of the corresponding property in members of the class.

(3) It is possible for the scientist to intuit correctly this isomorphism of language and reality.

* Aristotle included mechanics in the set of composite sciences at *Posterior Analytics* 76ᵃ23–5 and *Metaphysics* 1078ᵃ14–7, but did not mention mechanics at *Physics* 194ᵃ7–11.

Aristotle's position is plausible. We do believe that 'all men are mammals', for instance, is necessarily true, whereas 'all ravens are black' is only accidentally true. Aristotle would say that although a man could not possibly be a non-mammal, a raven might well be non-black. But, as noted above, although Aristotle did give examples of this kind to contrast "essential predication" and "accidental predication", he failed to formulate a general criterion to determine which predications are essential.

Aristotle bequeathed to his successors a faith that, because the first principles of the sciences mirror relations in nature which could not be other than they are, these principles are incapable of being false. To be sure, he could not authenticate this faith. Despite this, Aristotle's position that scientific laws state necessary truths has been widely influential in the history of science.

REFERENCES

1 Aristotle, *Posterior Analytics*, 89^{b}10–20.
2 Ibid., 78^{a}38–78^{b}3.
3 Ibid., 71^{b}20–72^{a}5.
4 Ibid., 73^{a}25–73^{b}15.

2
The Pythagorean Orientation

PLATO (428/7–348/7 B.C.) was born into a distinguished Athenian family. In early life he held political ambitions, but became disillusioned, first with the tyranny of the Thirty, and then with the restored democracy which executed his friend Socrates in 399 B.C. In later life, Plato made two visits to Syracuse in the hope of educating to responsible statesmanship its youthful ruler. The visits were not a success.

Plato founded the Academy in 387 B.C. Under his leadership, this Athenian institution became a centre for research in mathematics, science, and political theory. Plato himself contributed dialogues that deal with the entire range of human experience. In the *Timaeus*, he presented as a "likely story" a picture of a universe structured by geometrical harmonies.

PTOLEMY (CLAUDIUS PTOLEMAEUS, *c.* 100–*c.* 178) was an Alexandrian astronomer about whose life virtually nothing is known. His principal work, *The Almagest*, is an encyclopedic synthesis of the results of Greek astronomy, a synthesis brought up to date with new observations. In addition, he introduced the concept of circular motion with uniform angular velocity about an equant point, a point at some distance from the centre of the circle. By using equants, in addition to epicycles and deferents, he was able to predict with fair accuracy the motions of the planets against the zodiac.

THE PYTHAGOREAN VIEW OF NATURE

IT probably is not possible for a scientist to interrogate nature from a wholly disinterested standpoint. Even if he has no particular axe to grind, he is likely to have a distinctive way of viewing nature. The "Pythagorean Orientation" is a way of viewing nature which has been very influential in the history of science. A scientist who has this orientation believes that the "real" is the mathematical harmony that is present in nature. The committed Pythagorean is convinced that knowledge of this mathematical harmony is insight into the fundamental structure of the universe. A persuasive expression of this point of view is Galileo's declaration that

philosophy is written in this grand book—I mean the universe—which stands continually open to our gaze, but it cannot be understood unless one first learns to comprehend the language and interpret the characters in which it is written. It is written in the language of mathematics, and its characters are triangles, circles, and other geometrical figures, without which it is humanly impossible to understand a single word of it.[1]

This orientation originated when Pythagoras, or his followers, discovered that musical harmonies could be correlated with mathematical ratios, i.e.,

interval	ratio
octave	2 : 1
fifth	3 : 2
fourth	4 : 3

The early Pythagoreans found, moreover, that these ratios hold regardless of whether the notes are produced by vibrating strings or resonating air columns. Subsequently, Pythagorean natural philosophers read musical harmonies into the universe at large. They associated the motions of the heavenly bodies with sounds in such a way that there results a "harmony of the spheres".

PLATO AND THE PYTHAGOREAN ORIENTATION

Plato sometimes has been condemned for supposedly promulgating a philosophical orientation detrimental to the progress of science. The orientation in question is a turning away from the study of the world as revealed in sense experience, in favour of the contemplation of abstract ideas. Detractors of Plato often emphasize *Republic*

529–30, where Socrates recommends a shift in attention from the transient phenomena of the heavens to the timeless purity of geometrical relations. But, as Dicks has pointed out, Socrates' advice is given in the context of a discussion of the ideal education of prospective rulers. In this context, Plato is concerned to emphasize those types of study which promote the development of the capacity for abstract thought.[2] Thus he contrasts "pure geometry" with its practical application, and geometrical astronomy with the observation of light streaks in the sky.

Everyone is in agreement that Plato was dissatisfied with a "merely empirical" knowledge of the succession and coexistence of phenomena. This sort of "knowledge" must be transcended in such a way that the underlying rational order becomes manifest. The point of division among interpreters of Plato is whether it is required of the seeker of this deeper truth to turn away from what is given in sense experience. My own view is that Plato would say 'no' at this point, and would maintain that this "deeper knowledge" is to be achieved by uncovering the pattern which "lies hidden within" phenomena. At any rate, it is doubtful that Plato would have been an influence in the history of science had he not been interpreted in this manner by subsequent natural philosophers.

This influence has been expressed primarily in terms of general attitudes towards science. Natural philosophers who counted themselves "Platonists" believed in the underlying rationality of the universe and the importance of discovering it. And they drew sustenance from what they took to be Plato's similar conviction. In the late Middle Ages and the Renaissance, this Platonism was an important corrective both to the denigration of science within religious circles and to the preoccupation with disputation based on standard texts within academic circles.

In addition, commitment to Plato's philosophy tended to reinforce a Pythagorean orientation toward science. Indeed, the Pythagorean orientation became influential in the Christian West largely as a result of a marriage of Plato's *Timaeus* and Holy Scripture. In the *Timaeus*, Plato described the creation of the universe by a benevolent Demiurge, who impressed a mathematical pattern upon a formless primordial matter. This account was appropriated by Christian apologists, who identified the pattern with the Divine Plan of Creation and repressed the emphasis on a primordial matter. For those who accepted this synthesis, the task of the natural philosopher is to uncover the mathematical pattern upon which the universe is ordered.

Plato himself suggested in the *Timaeus* that the five "elements"— four terrestrial and one celestial—may be correlated with the five regular solids.

| Tetrahedron | Cube | Octahedron | Icosahedron | Dodecahedron |
| (fire) | (earth) | (air) | (water) | (celestial matter) |

He assigned the tetrahedron to fire, because the tetrahedron is the regular solid with the sharpest angles, and because fire is the most penetrating of elements. He assigned the cube to Earth, because it takes more effort to tip over a cube on its base than it does to tip over any one of the remaining three regular solids, and because Earth is the most "solid" of the elements. Plato used similar reasoning to assign the octahedron to air, the icosahedron to water, and the dodecahedron to celestial matter. In addition, he suggested that transformations among water, air, and fire result from a "dissolution" of each equilateral triangular face of the respective regular solids into six 30°–60°–90° triangles,* with subsequent recombination of these smaller triangles to form the faces of other regular solids. Plato's explanation of matter and its properties in terms of geometrical figures is very much in the Pythagorean tradition.

THE TRADITION OF "SAVING THE APPEARANCES"

The Pythagorean natural philosopher believes that mathematical relations which fit phenomena count as explanations of why things

* Viz.:

are as they are. This point of view has had opposition, almost from its inception, from a rival point of view. This rival view is that mathematical hypotheses must be distinguished from theories about the structure of the universe. On this view, it is one thing to "save the appearances" by superimposing mathematical relations on phenomena, but quite another thing to explain why the phenomena are as they are.

This distinction between physically true theories and hypotheses which save the appearances was made by Geminus in the first century B.C. Geminus outlined two approaches to the study of celestial phenomena. One is the approach of the physicist, who derives the motions of the heavenly bodies from their essential natures. The second is the approach of the astronomer, who derives the motions of the heavenly bodies from mathematical figures and motions. He declared that

it is no part of the business of an astronomer to know what is by nature suited to a position of rest, and what sort of bodies are apt to move, but he introduces hypotheses under which some bodies remain fixed, while others move, and then considers to which hypotheses the phenomena actually observed in the heaven will correspond.[3]

Ptolemy on Mathematical Models

In the second century A.D., Claudius Ptolemy formulated a series of mathematical models, one for each planet then known. One important feature of the models is the use of epicycle-deferent circles to reproduce the apparent motions of the planets against the zodiac. On the epicycle-deferent model, the planet P moves along an epicyclic circle, the centre of which moves along a deferent circle around the earth. By adjusting the speeds of revolution of the points P and C, Ptolemy could reproduce the observed periodic retrograde motion of the planet. In passing from A to B along the epicycle, the planet appears to an observer on earth to reverse the direction of its motion against the background stars.

Ptolemy emphasized that more than one mathematical model can be constructed to save the appearances of planetary motions. He noted, in particular, that a moving-eccentric system can be constructed which is mathematically equivalent to a given epicycle-deferent system.*

---

* Ptolemy credited Apollonius of Perga (*fl.* 220 B.C.) with the first demonstration of this equivalence.

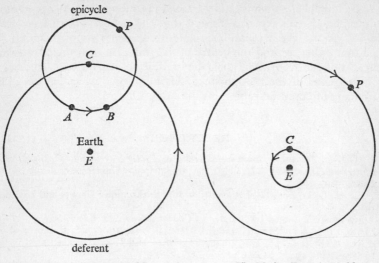

The Epicycle-Deferent Model   *The Moving-Eccentric Model*

In the moving-eccentric model, planet P moves along a circle centred on eccentric point C, which point C moves, with opposite-directed motion, along a circle centred on the Earth E. Since the two models are mathematically equivalent, the astronomer is at liberty to employ whichever model is the more convenient.

A tradition arose in astronomy that the astronomer should construct mathematical models to save the appearances, but should not theorize about the "real motions" of the planets. This tradition owed much to Ptolemy's work on planetary motions. Ptolemy himself, however, did not consistently defend this position. He did hint in the *Almagest* that his mathematical models were computational devices only, and that he was not to be understood as claiming that the planets actually describe epicyclic motions in physical space. But in a later work, the *Hypotheses Planetarum*, he claimed that his complicated system of circles revealed the structure of physical reality.

Ptolemy's uneasiness about restricting astronomy to saving the appearances was echoed by Proclus, a fifth-century Neoplatonist. Proclus complained that astronomers had subverted proper scientific method. Instead of deducing conclusions from self-evident axioms, on the model of geometry, they frame hypotheses solely to accommodate phenomena. Proclus insisted that the proper axiom for astronomy is the Aristotelian principle that every simple motion is motion either around the centre of the universe or toward or away from this centre. And he took the inability of astronomers to derive the motions of the planets from this axiom as an indication of a divinely imposed limitation on the human mind.

REFERENCES

[1] Galileo, *The Assayer*, trans. by S. Drake, in *The Controversy on the Comets of 1618*, trans. by S. Drake and C. D. O'Malley (Philadelphia: University of Pennsylvania Press, 1960), 183–4.

[2] D. R. Dicks, *Early Greek Astronomy to Aristotle* (London: Thames and Hudson, 1970), 104–7.

[3] Geminus is quoted by Simplicius, *Commentary on Aristotle's Physics*, in T. L. Heath, *Aristarchus of Samos* (Oxford: Clarendon Press, 1913), 275–6; reprinted in *A Source Book in Greek Science*, ed. by M. Cohen and I. E. Drabkin (New York: McGraw-Hill, 1948), 91.

3
The Ideal of Deductive Systematization

EUCLID (*fl.* 300 B.C.), according to Proclus, taught and founded a school at Alexandria. His most important surviving work is the *Elements*. It is not possible to say with any assurance to what extent this work was a codification of existing geometrical knowledge and to what extent it was the fruit of original research. It seems likely that, in addition to setting out geometry as a deductive system, Euclid constructed a number of original proofs.

ARCHIMEDES (287–212 B.C.), the son of an astronomer, was born at Syracuse. It is believed that he spent some time at Alexandria, perhaps studying with the successors of Euclid. Upon his return to Syracuse, he devoted himself to research in pure and applied mathematics.

Archimedes' fame in Antiquity derived in large measure from his prowess as a military engineer. It is reported that catapults of his design were used effectively against the Romans during the siege of Syracuse. Archimedes himself was said to prize more highly his abstract investigations of conic sections, hydrostatics, and equilibria involving the law of the lever. According to legend, Archimedes was slain by Roman soldiers while he was contemplating a geometrical problem.

A widely held thesis among ancient writers was that the structure of a completed science ought to be a deductive system of statements. Aristotle had emphasized the deduction of conclusions from first principles. Many writers in late Antiquity believed that the ideal of deductive systematization had been realized in the geometry of Euclid and the statics of Archimedes.

Euclid and Archimedes had formulated systems of statements—comprising axioms, definitions, and theorems—organized so that the truth of the theorems follows from the assumed truth of the axioms. For example, Euclid proved that his axioms, together with definitions of such terms as 'angle' and 'triangle', imply that the sum of the angles of a triangle is equal to two right angles. And Archimedes proved from his axioms on the lever that two unequal weights balance at distances from the fulcrum that are inversely proportional to their weights.

Three aspects of the ideal of deductive systematization are (1) that the axioms and theorems are deductively related; (2) that the axioms themselves are self-evident truths; and (3) that the theorems agree with observations. Philosophers of science have taken different positions on the second and third aspects, but there has been general agreement on the first aspect.

One cannot subscribe to the deductive ideal without accepting the requirement that theorems be related deductively to axioms. Euclid and Archimedes utilized two important techniques to prove theorems from their axioms: *reductio ad absurdum* arguments, and a method of exhaustion.

The *reductio ad absurdum* technique of proving theorem 'T' is to assume that 'not T' is true and then deduce from 'not T' and the axioms of the system both a statement and its negation. If two contradictory statements can be deduced in this way, and if the axioms of the system are true, then 'T' must be true as well.*

The method of exhaustion is an extension of the *reductio ad absurdum* technique. It consists of showing that each possible contrary of a theorem has consequences that are inconsistent with the axioms of a system.†

---

* Archimedes used a *reductio ad absurdum* argument to prove that 'weights that balance at equal distances from a fulcrum are equal' ('T'). He began by assuming the truth of the contradictory statement that 'the balancing weights are of unequal magnitude' ('not T'), and then showed that 'not T' is false, because it has implications that contradict one of the axioms of the system. For if 'not T' were true, one could decrease the weight of the greater so that the two weights were of equal magnitude. But axiom 3 states that, if one of two weights initially in equilibrium is decreased, then the lever inclines toward the undiminished weight. The lever no longer would be in equilibrium. But this contradicts 'not T', thereby establishing 'T'.[1]

† Archimedes used the method of exhaustion to prove that the area of a circle is equal to the area of a right triangle whose base is the radius of the circle and whose altitude is its circumference. Archimedes proved this theorem by showing that, if one assumes that the area of the circle either is greater than or is less than that of the triangle, contradictions ensue within the axiom system of geometry.[2] See diagram on page 25.

With regard to the requirement of deductive relations between axioms and theorems, Euclid's geometry was deficient. Euclid deduced a number of his theorems by appealing to the operation of superimposing figures to establish their congruence. But no reference is made in the axioms to this operation of superposition. Thus Euclid "proved" some of his theorems by going outside the axiom system. Euclid's geometry was recast into rigorous deductive form by David Hilbert in the latter part of the nineteenth century. In Hilbert's reformulation, every theorem of the system is a deductive consequence of the axioms and definitions.

A second, more controversial aspect of the ideal of deductive systematization is the requirement that the axioms themselves be self evident truths. This requirement was stated clearly by Aristotle, who insisted that the first principles of the respective sciences be necessary truths.

The requirement that the axioms of deductive systems be self-evident truths was consistent with the Pythagorean approach to natural philosophy as well. The committed Pythagorean believes that there exist in nature mathematical relations that can be discovered by reason. From this standpoint, it is natural to insist that the starting-points of deductive systematization be those mathematical relations which have been found to underlie phenomena.

A different attitude was taken by those who followed the tradition of saving the appearances in mathematical astronomy. They

Archimedes' Circle – Triangle Relation

rejected the Aristotelian requirement. To save appearances it suffices that the deductive consequences of the axioms should agree with observations. That the axioms themselves are implausible, or even false, is irrelevant.

The third aspect of the ideal of deductive systematization is that the deductive system should make contact with reality. Certainly Euclid and Archimedes intended to prove theorems which had practical application. Indeed Archimedes was famous for his application of the law of the lever to the construction of catapults for military purposes.

But to make contact with the realm of experience it is necessary that at least some of the terms of the deductive system should refer to objects and relations in the world. It seems just to have been assumed by Euclid, Archimedes, and their immediate successors that such terms as 'point', 'line', 'weight', and 'rod' do have empirical correlates. Archimedes, for instance, does not mention the problems involved in giving an empirical interpretation to his theorems on the lever. He made no comments on the limitations that must be imposed on the nature of the lever itself. And yet the theorems he derived are confirmed experimentally only for rods that do not bend appreciably, and which have a uniform weight distribution. Archimedes' theorems apply strictly only to an "idealized lever" which, in principle, cannot be realized in experience, namely, an infinitely rigid, but mass-less, rod.

It may be that Archimedes' preoccupation with laws applicable to this "ideal lever" reflects a philosophical tradition in which a contrast is drawn between the unruly complexities of phenomena and the timeless purity of formal relationships. This tradition often was reinforced by the ontological claim that the phenomenal realm is at best an "imitation" or "reflection" of the "real world". Primary responsibility for promulgating this point of view rests with Plato and his interpreters. This dualism had important repercussions in the thought of Galileo and Descartes.

REFERENCES

[1] T. L. Heath, ed., *The Works of Archimedes* (New York: Dover Publications, 1912), 189–90.
[2] Ibid., 91–3.

4
Atomism and the Concept of Underlying Mechanism

As noted above, some followers of Plato construed the world to be an imperfect reflection of an underlying reality. A more radical discontinuity was suggested by the atomists Democritus and Leucippus. For the atomists, the relation between appearance and reality was not the relation between an original and an imperfect copy. Rather, they believed that objects and relations in the "real world" were *different in kind* from the world we know by means of the senses.

What is real, according to the atomists, is the motion of atoms through the void. It is the motions of atoms which cause our perceptual experience of colours, odours, and tastes. Were there no such motions, there would be no perceptual experience. Moreover, the atoms themselves have only the properties of size, shape, impenetrability, and motion, and the propensity to enter into various combinations and associations. Unlike macroscopic objects, atoms can be neither penetrated nor subdivided.

The atomists attributed phenomenal changes to the association and dissociation of atoms. For instance, they attributed the salty taste of some foodstuffs to the setting free of large, jagged atoms, and the ability of fire to penetrate bodies to the rapid motions of tiny, spherical fire-atoms.[1]

Several aspects of the atomists' programme have been important in the development of subsequent views of scientific method. One influential aspect of atomism is the idea that observed changes can be explained by reference to processes occurring at a more elementary level of organization. This became an item of belief for many natural philosophers in the seventeenth century. That sub-macroscopic interactions cause macroscopic changes was affirmed by Gassendi, Boyle, and Newton, among others.

Moreover, the ancient atomists realized, tacitly at least, that one cannot explain adequately qualities and processes at one level merely by postulating that the same qualities and processes are present at a deeper level. For instance, one cannot account satisfactorily for the colours of objects by attributing the colours to the presence of coloured atoms.

A further important aspect of the atomists' programme is the reduction of qualitative changes at the macroscopic level to quantitative changes at the atomic level. Atomists agreed with Pythagoreans that scientific explanations ought to be given in terms of geometrical and numerical relationships.

Two factors weighed against any widespread acceptance of the classical version of atomism. The first factor was the uncompromising materialism of this philosophy. By explaining sensation and even thought in terms of the motions of atoms, the atomists challenged man's self-understanding. Atomism seemed to leave no place for spiritual values. Surely the values of friendship, courage, and worship cannot be reduced to the concourse of atoms. Moreover, the atomists left no place in science for considerations of purpose, whether natural or divine.

The second factor was the *ad hoc* nature of the atomists' explanations. They offered a picture-preference, a way of looking at phenomena, but there was no way to check the accuracy of the picture. Consider the dissolving of salt in water. The strongest argument advanced by classical atomists was that the effect *could be* produced by dispersal of salt-atoms into the liquid. However, the classical atomists could not explain why salt dissolves in water whereas sand does not. Of course they could say that salt-atoms fit into the interstices between water-atoms whereas sand-atoms do not. But the critics of atomism would dismiss this "explanation" as merely another way of saying that salt dissolves in water whereas sand does not.

REFERENCES

[1] G. S. Kirk and J. E. Raven, *The Presocratic Philosophers* (Cambridge: Cambridge University Press, 1962), 420–3.

5
Affirmation and Development of Aristotle's Method in the Medieval Period

ROBERT GROSSETESTE (*c.* 1168–1253) was a scholar and teacher at Oxford who became a statesman of the Church. He was Chancellor of Oxford University (1215–21), and from 1224 served as lecturer in philosophy to the Franciscan order. Grosseteste was the first medieval scholar to analyse the problems of induction and verification. He wrote commentaries on Aristotle's *Posterior Analytics* and *Physics*, prepared translations of the *De Caelo* and *Nicomachean Ethics*, and composed treatises on calendar reform, optics, heat, and sound. He developed a Neoplatonic "metaphysics of light" in which causal agency is attributed to the multiplication and outward spherical diffusion of "species", upon analogy to the propagation of light from a source. Grosseteste became Bishop of Lincoln in 1235 and redirected his considerable energies so as to include ecclesiastical administration.

ROGER BACON (*c.* 1214–1292) studied at Oxford and then Paris, where he taught and wrote analyses of various Aristotelian works. In 1247 he returned to Oxford, where he studied various languages and the sciences, with particular emphasis on optics. Pope Clement IV, on learning of Bacon's proposed unification of the sciences in the service of theology, requested a copy of Bacon's work. Bacon had not yet put his views on paper, but he rapidly composed and dispatched to the Pope the *Opus Maius* and two companion works (1268). Unfortunately the Pope died before having assessed Bacon's contribution.

Bacon appears to have antagonized his superiors in the Franciscan order by his sharp criticism of the intellectual capabilities of his colleagues. Moreover, his enthusiasm for alchemy, astrology, and the apocalypticism of Joachim of Floris rendered him suspect. It is likely, although not beyond doubt, that he spent several of his later years under confinement.

JOHN DUNS SCOTUS (*c.* 1265–1308) entered the Franciscan order in 1280 and was ordained a priest in 1291. He studied at Oxford and Paris, where he received a doctorate in theology in 1305, despite having been banished from Paris for a time for failing to support the King in a dispute with the Pope over the taxation of Church lands. In company with many other medieval writers, Duns Scotus sought to assimilate Aristotelian philosophy to Christian doctrine.

WILLIAM OF OCKHAM (*c.* 1280–1349) studied and taught at Oxford. He soon became a focus of controversy within the Church. He attacked the Pope's claim of temporal supremacy, insisting on the divinely ordained independence of civil authority. He appealed to the prior pronouncements of Pope Nicholas III in a dispute with Pope John XXII over apostolic poverty. And he defended the nominalist position that universals have objective value only in so far as they are present in the mind. Ockham took refuge in Bavaria for a time while his writings were under examination at Avignon. No formal condemnation took place, however.

NICOLAUS OF AUTRECOURT (*c.* 1300–after 1350) studied and lectured at the University of Paris, where he developed a critique of the prevalent doctrines of substance and causality. In 1346 he was sentenced by the Avignon Curia to burn his writings and to recant certain condemned doctrines before the faculty of the University of Paris. Nicolaus complied, and, curiously enough, subsequently was appointed deacon at the Cathedral of Metz (1350).

PRIOR to 1150, Aristotle was known to scholars in the Latin West primarily as a logician. Plato was held to be the pre-eminent philosopher of nature. But commencing about 1150, Aristotle's writings on science and scientific method began to be translated from Arabic and Greek sources into Latin. Centres of translating activity arose in Spain and Italy. By 1270, the extensive Aristotelian corpus had been translated into Latin. The impact of this achievement on intellectual life in the West was very great indeed. Aristotle's writings on science and scientific method provided scholars with a wealth of new insights. So much so that for several generations the standard presentation of a work on a particular science took the form of a commentary on the corresponding study by Aristotle.

Aristotle's most important writing on the philosophy of science is the *Posterior Analytics*, a work that became available to western scholars in the latter part of the twelfth century. During the next three centuries, writers on scientific method addressed themselves to the problems that had been formulated by Aristotle. In particular, medieval commentators discussed and criticized Aristotle's view of scientific procedure, his position on evaluating competing explanations, and his claim that scientific knowledge is necessary truth.

THE INDUCTIVE-DEDUCTIVE PATTERN OF SCIENTIFIC INQUIRY

Robert Grosseteste and Roger Bacon, the two most influential thirteenth-century writers on scientific method, affirmed Aristotle's inductive-deductive pattern of scientific inquiry. Grosseteste referred to the inductive stage as a "resolution" of phenomena into constituent elements, and to the deductive stage as a "composition" in which these elements are combined to reconstruct the original phenomena.[1] Subsequent writers often referred to Aristotle's theory of scientific procedure as the "Method of Resolution and Composition".

Grosseteste applied the Aristotelian theory of procedure to the problem of spectral colours. He noted that the spectra seen in rainbows, mill-wheel sprays, boat-oar sprays, and the spectra produced by passing sunlight through water-filled glass spheres, shared certain common characteristics. Proceeding by induction, he "resolved" three elements which are common to the various instances. These elements are (1) that the spectra are associated with transparent spheres, (2) that different colours result from the refraction of light through different angles, and (3) that the colours produced lie on the arc of a circle. He then was able to "compose" the general features of this class of phenomena from the above three elements.[2]

Roger Bacon's "Second Prerogative" of Experimental Science

Grosseteste's Method of Resolution specifies an inductive ascent from statements about phenomena to elements from which the phenomena may be reconstructed. Grosseteste's pupil Roger Bacon emphasized that successful application of this inductive procedure depends on accurate and extensive factual knowledge. Bacon suggested that the factual base of a science often may be augmented by active experimentation. The use of experimentation to increase knowledge of phenomena is the second of Bacon's "Three Prerogatives of Experimental Science".[3]

Bacon praised a certain "master of experimentation" whose work constituted a realization of the second prerogative. The individual cited probably was Petrus of Maricourt.[4] Petrus had demonstrated, among other things, that breaking a magnetic needle crosswise into two fragments produces two new magnets, each with its own north pole and south pole. Bacon emphasized that discoveries such as this increase the observational base from which the elements of magnetism may be induced.

Had Bacon restricted his praise of experimentation to this kind of investigation, he would merit recognition as a champion of experimental inquiry. However, Bacon often placed experimentation in the service of alchemy, and he made extravagant and unsupported claims for the results of alchemical experiments. He declared, for instance, that one triumph of "Experimental Science" was the discovery of a substance that removes the impurities from base metals such that pure gold remains.[5]

The Inductive Methods of Agreement and Difference

Aristotle had insisted that explanatory principles should be induced from observations. An important contribution of medieval scholars was to outline additional inductive techniques for discovering explanatory principles.

Robert Grosseteste, for example, suggested that one good way to determine whether a particular herb has a purgative effect would be to examine numerous cases in which the herb is administered under conditions where no other purgative agents are present.[6] It would be difficult to implement this test, and there is no evidence that Grosseteste attempted to do so. But he must be credited with outlining an inductive procedure which centuries later came to be known as "Mill's Joint Method of Agreement and Difference".

In the fourteenth century, John Duns Scotus outlined an inductive Method of Agreement, and William of Ockham outlined an inductive Method of Difference. They regarded these methods as aids in the "resolution" of phenomena. As such, they are procedures intended to supplement the inductive procedures which Aristotle had discussed.

Duns Scotus's Method of Agreement. Duns Scotus's Method of Agreement is a technique for analysing a number of instances in which a particular effect occurs. The procedure is to list the various circumstances that are present each time the effect occurs, and to look for some one circumstance that is present in every instance.[7] Duns Scotus would hold that, if a listing of circumstances has the form

Instance	Circumstances	Effect
1	*ABCD*	*e*
2	*ACE*	*e*
3	*ABEF*	*e*
4	*ADF*	*e*

then the investigator is entitled to conclude that *e can be* the effect of cause *A*.

Duns Scotus's claims for his Method of Agreement were quite modest. He held that the most that can be established by an application of the method is an "aptitudinal union" between an effect and an accompanying circumstance. By applying the schema, a scientist may conclude, for instance, that the moon is a body that *can be* eclipsed, or that a certain kind of herb *can have* a bitter taste.[8] But application of the schema alone can establish neither that the moon necessarily must be eclipsed, nor that every sample of the herb necessarily is bitter.

Paradoxically, Duns Scotus both augmented the Method of Resolution and undercut confidence in inductively established correlations. His theological convictions were responsible for the latter emphasis. He insisted that God can accomplish anything which does not involve a contradiction, and that uniformities in nature exist only by the forbearance of God. Moreover, God could, if He wished, short-circuit a regularity and produce an effect directly without the presence of the usual cause. It was for this reason that Duns Scotus held that the Method of Agreement can establish only aptitudinal unions within experience.

William of Ockham's Method of Difference. Emphasis on the omnipotence of God is still more pronounced in the writings of William of Ockham. Ockham repeatedly insisted that God can accomplish anything that can be done without contradiction. In agreement with Duns Scotus, he held that the scientist can establish by induction only aptitudinal unions among phenomena.

Ockham formulated a procedure for drawing conclusions about aptitudinal unions according to a Method of Difference. Ockham's method is to compare two instances—one instance in which the effect is present, and a second instance in which the effect is not present. If it can be shown that there is a circumstance present when the effect is present and absent when the effect is absent, e.g.,

Instance	Circumstances	Effect
1	ABC	e
2	AB	-

then the investigator is entitled to conclude that the circumstance *C can be* the cause of effect *e*.

Ockham maintained that, in the ideal case, knowledge of an aptitudinal union can be established on the basis of just one observed association. He noted, though, that in such a case one would have to be certain that all other possible causes of the effect in question are absent. He observed that in practice it is difficult to determine whether two sets of circumstances differ in one respect only. For that reason, he urged that numerous cases be investigated in order to minimize the possibility that some unrecognized factor is responsible for the occurrence of the effect.[9]

EVALUATION OF COMPETING EXPLANATIONS

Grosseteste and Roger Bacon, in addition to restating Aristotle's inductive-deductive pattern of scientific inquiry, also made original contributions to the problem of evaluating competing explanations. They recognized that a statement about an effect may be deduced from more than one set of premises. Aristotle, too, had been aware of this, and had insisted that genuine scientific explanations state causal relationships.

Roger Bacon's "First Prerogative" of Experimental Science

Both Grosseteste and Bacon recommended that a third stage of inquiry be added to Aristotle's inductive-deductive procedure. In this third stage of inquiry, the principles induced by "resolution" are submitted to the test of further experience. Bacon called this testing procedure the "first prerogative" of experimental science.[10] This was a valuable methodological insight, and constituted a significant advance over Aristotle's theory of procedure. Aristotle had been content to deduce statements about the same phenomena which serve as the starting-points of an investigation. Grosseteste and Bacon demanded further experimental testing of the principles reached by induction.

At the beginning of the fourteenth century, Theodoric of Freiberg made a striking application of Bacon's first prerogative. Theodoric believed that the rainbow is caused by a combination of refraction and reflection of sunlight by individual raindrops. In order to test this hypothesis, he filled hollow crystalline spheres with water, and placed them in the path of the sun's rays. He reproduced with these model drops both primary rainbows and secondary rainbows. Theodoric demonstrated that the reproduced secondary rainbows had their order of colours reversed, and that the angle between incident and emergent rays for the secondary rainbows was eleven degrees greater than for the primary rainbows. This is in good agreement with what is observed in naturally occurring rainbows.[11]

ray of
secondary
rainbow

ray of
primary
rainbow

Theodoric's Model Raindrop

Unfortunately, Grosseteste and Bacon themselves frequently ignored their own counsel. Bacon, in particular, often appealed to *a priori* considerations and the authority of previous writers, rather than to additional experimental testing. For example, after declaring that experimental science is admirably suited to establish conclusions about the nature of the rainbow, Bacon insisted that there must be just five colours in the rainbow because the number five is the ideal number to set forth a variation in qualities.[12]

Grosseteste's Method of Falsification

Grosseteste noted that if a statement about an effect can be deduced from more than one set of premisses, then the best approach is to eliminate all but one of the explanations. He maintained that if a hypothesis implies certain consequences, and if these consequences can be shown to be false, then the hypothesis itself must be false. Logicians have given the name '*modus tollens*' to this type of deductive argument:

$$\text{If } H \text{ then } C$$
$$\underline{\text{not } C}$$
$$\therefore \text{ not } H$$

Given a group of hypotheses, each of which can be used as a premiss to deduce a given effect, it may be possible to eliminate all hypotheses but one by means of *modus tollens* arguments. To do this one would have to show that every hypothesis but one implies *other* consequences which are known to be false.

Grosseteste applied the Method of Falsification to support a hypothesis about the generation of the sun's heat. According to Grosseteste, there are just three modes of generating heat: by conduction from a hot body, "by motion", and by a concentration of rays. He believed that the sun generates heat by a concentration of rays, and he sought to exclude the other two possibilities by *modus tollens* arguments. He "falsified" the conduction hypothesis by the following argument:

If the sun generates heat by conduction, then the adjacent celestial matter is heated and undergoes a change of quality.

But the adjacent celestial matter is immutable and does not undergo a change of quality.

Therefore, the sun does not generate heat by conduction.[13]

This argument has the *modus tollens* form, and hence is valid—if its premisses are true, then its conclusion must be true as well. However, the second premiss, which asserts the immutability of the adjacent celestial matter, is false. Grosseteste's argument did not prove false the conduction hypothesis. And his argument to falsify the motion hypothesis failed for a similar reason.[14]

Grosseteste was not the first scholar to use *modus tollens* arguments to falsify rival hypotheses. Philosophers and mathematicians had made use of this technique since the time of Euclid.* Grosseteste's achievement was the systematic application of this technique to supplement Aristotle's evaluation procedures for scientific hypotheses.

In spite of the fact that Grosseteste's numerous applications of *modus tollens* arguments are unconvincing in the light of current scientific knowledge, the method of falsification itself was widely influential. The fourteenth-century scholar John Buridan, for example, used a *modus tollens* argument to falsify a hypothesis about projectile motion that had been mentioned, but not defended, by Aristotle. On this hypothesis, the air in front of the projected body rushes around to the rear in order to prevent the occurrence of a vacuum, thereby pushing forward the projectile. Buridan pointed out that if this hypothesis were true, then a projectile with a blunt posterior end should move faster than one with two pointed ends. He insisted that a projectile with a blunt posterior end does not travel faster, although he did not claim to have performed experiments with the two types of projectiles.[16]

Ockham's "Razor"

A large number of medieval writers defended the principle that nature always chooses the simplest path. Grosseteste, for instance, maintained that the angle of refraction must be one half of the angle

---

* An example is Euclid's proof that there is no greatest prime number. Euclid began by assuming the contradictory: that there does exist a greatest prime number, denoted by N. He then formed the number

$$N' = (2 \times 3 \times 5 \times 7 \times 11 \times \ldots N) + 1,$$

in which the product within parentheses includes every prime number up to and including N. He then formed the following *modus tollens* argument:

If N is the greatest prime number, then N' (which is greater than N) is not a prime number.

But N' is a prime number (since division of N' by any prime number leaves a remainder of 1).

Therefore, N is not the greatest prime number.[15]

of incidence for a light ray passing into a denser medium. He believed that this 1:2 ratio holds because nature pursues the simplest course, and because the 1:1 ratio is unavailable since it governs reflection.[17]

William of Ockham opposed this tendency to read into nature human ideas about simplicity. He felt that to insist that nature always follows the simplest path is to limit God's power. God may very well choose to achieve effects in the most complicated of ways.

For this reason, Ockham shifted emphasis on simplicity from the course of nature to theories which are formulated about it. Ockham used simplicity as a criterion of concept-formation and theory-construction. He held that superfluous concepts are to be eliminated, and suggested that the simpler of two theories that account for a type of phenomena is to be preferred. Subsequent writers often referred to this methodological principle as "Ockham's Razor".

Ockham applied his Razor in the medieval debates on the nature of projectile motion. One view was that a projectile's motion is caused by an acquired "impetus" which resides somehow in the projectile as long as it is in motion. Ockham held that impetus is a superfluous concept. According to Ockham, a statement about the 'motion of a body' is shorthand for a series of statements that attribute to the body various positions at various times. And motion is not a property of a body, but is a relation which a body has to other bodies and to time. Since change of position is not a "property" of a body, there is no need to assign an efficient cause to this relative displacement. Ockham maintained that to say "a body moves because of an acquired impetus" is to say no more than "a body moves", and he recommended elimination from physics of the concept of impetus.[18]

THE CONTROVERSY ABOUT NECESSARY TRUTH

Aristotle had insisted that because a "natural necessity" orders the relations among the species and genera of objects and events, the appropriate verbal expression of these relations must have the status of necessary truth. According to Aristotle, the first principles of the sciences are not merely contingently true. They are incapable of being false, because they mirror relations in nature which could not be other than they are.

An important fourteenth-century development in the philosophy of science was a reassessment of the cognitive status of scientific interpretations. John Duns Scotus, William of Ockham, and Nicolaus of

Autrecourt, among others, sought to determine what kinds of statements, if any, are necessary truths. Their point of departure was Aristotle's position that the first principles of the sciences are self-evident, necessary representations of the way things are.

Duns Scotus on the "Aptitudinal Union" of Phenomena

Duns Scotus insisted on a distinction between the origin of first principles and the warrant for their status as necessary truths. He agreed with Aristotle that knowledge of first principles arises out of sense experience, but he added that the necessary status of these principles is independent of the truth of reports about sense experience. According to Duns Scotus, sense experience provides occasions for recognizing the truth of a first principle, but sense experience is not evidence for this truth. Rather, a first principle is true in virtue of the meanings of its constituent terms. This is so, despite the fact that it is from experience that we learn the meanings of these terms.[19] For instance, that 'opaque bodies cast shadows' is self-evident to anyone who understands the meanings of the terms 'opaque', 'cast', and 'shadow'. Moreover, this principle is a necessary truth. To deny it is to formulate a self-contradiction. Duns Scotus held that not even God could cause a self-contradiction to be implemented in the world.

Duns Scotus held that two types of scientific generalizations are necessary truths: the first principles and their deductive consequences, and statements of aptitudinal unions of phenomena. By contrast, he held that empirical generalizations are contingent truths. For example, it is necessarily true that all ravens *can be* black, but it is only a matter of contingent fact that all ravens examined have been black.

Of course the scientist cannot rest content with knowledge of aptitudinal unions of phenomena. To say that ravens *can be* black or that the moon *can be* eclipsed is to say relatively little about ravens and the moon. Duns Scotus recognized this. He recommended that, wherever possible, generalizations be deduced from first principles. The two examples differ in this respect. That the moon is a body frequently eclipsed may be deduced from the first principles that opaque bodies cast shadows, and that the earth is an opaque body which frequently is interposed between the luminous sun and the moon. No such derivation is available in the case of black ravens.

Nicolaus of Autrecourt on Necessary Truth as Conforming to the Principle of Non-contradiction

Nicolaus of Autrecourt restricted the range of certain knowledge more severely than did Duns Scotus. Nicolaus's analysis was the culmination of a fourteenth-century erosion of confidence in what can be known to be necessarily true.

Nicolaus resolved to accept as necessary truths only those judgements that satisfy the Principle of Non-contradiction. Following Aristotle, he announced that the primary principle of reasoning is that contradictories cannot both be true.

But although Aristotle did state that the Principle of Non-contradiction is the ultimate principle of all demonstration, he also recognized that no conclusions about physical or biological phenomena can be deduced from this principle alone. Hence Aristotle included among the first principles of demonstration both general logical principles such as the Laws of Identity, Non-contradiction, and the Excluded Middle, and first principles proper to the respective sciences.

Nicolaus, however, refused to concede certainty to the inductively established first principles of the sciences, whether these principles state causal relations or mere aptitudinal unions of phenomena. He restricted certain knowledge to the Principle of Non-contradiction itself and those statements and arguments that "conform" to it. The only exceptions he allowed were the articles of faith.[20]

Nicolaus insisted that every scientific demonstration should conform to the principle that every statement of the form 'A and not A' is necessarily false. According to Nicolaus, an argument "conforms" to the Principle of Non-contradiction if, and only if, the conjunction of its premises and the negation of its conclusion

$$'(P_1 \cdot P_2 \cdot P_3 \cdot \ldots P_n) \cdot {\sim} C'$$

is a self-contradiction.* Logicians today accept this requirement as a necessary and sufficient condition of deductive validity.

Nicolaus held that every valid argument is reducible to the Principle of Non-contradiction either immediately or mediately. The reduction is immediate if the conclusion is identical with the premisses or a part of the premisses. For example, it is immediately

---

* The symbol '·' stands for the English 'and' in conjunctions of the form 'p and q' where p and q are individual sentences. The expression '${\sim}p$' stands for the English 'It is false that p'.

evident that arguments of the form $\dfrac{A}{\therefore A}$ and $\dfrac{A \cdot B \cdot C}{\therefore A}$ satisfy the Principle of Non-contradiction. The reduction is mediate in the case of syllogistic arguments. For example, given the syllogism

P_1— All quadrilaterals are polygons.
P_2— All squares are quadrilaterals.
_____
C —∴All squares are polygons.

the negation of the conclusion is inconsistent with the conjunction of the premises. However, it is not immediately evident that the statement '$(P_1 \cdot P_2) \cdot \sim C$' is a self-contradiction. The statement is a self-contradiction only because '$(P_1 \cdot P_2)$' implies 'C'.

On the basis of this analysis of the nature of deductive arguments, Nicolaus denied that a necessary knowledge of causal relations could be achieved. He pointed out that no information can be deduced from a set of premises except that information implied by, or "contained in", the premises. In this respect, deductive arguments are like orange-juicers—no more juice can be extracted than is present initially in the oranges. But since a cause is something distinct from its effect, one cannot deduce a statement about an effect from statements about its supposed cause. Nicolaus insisted that it is not possible to deduce that because a particular phenomenon occurred, it must be accompanied by, or followed by, some other phenomenon.

Nicolaus argued, moreover, that it is not possible to achieve a necessary knowledge of causal relations by application of the Method of Agreement. He insisted that it cannot be established that a correlation which has been observed to hold must continue to hold in the future.[21] Duns Scotus, of course, could have accepted Nicolaus's critique without abandoning his own position, for he claimed to establish only aptitudinal unions between two types of phenomena.

The conclusion of Nicolaus's analysis is that no necessary knowledge of causal relations can be achieved. Statements about causes do not imply statements about effects, and inductive arguments do not prove that an observed correlation must hold.

Nicolaus declared that he hoped that his critique of what can be known with certainty would be of service to the Christian faith. He noted with disapproval that scholars spent entire lifetimes in the study of Aristotle. He suggested that it would be better if this energy were expended to improve the faith and morals of the community.[22]

Perhaps for this reason, he appended to his critique a "probable" theory of the universe based on classical atomism. Nicolaus wished to show, not only that Aristotle's science was not a science of certainties, but also that Aristotle's view of the universe was not even the most probable of world-views.

REFERENCES

[1] A. C. Crombie, *Robert Grosseteste and the Origins of Experimental Science* (*1100–1700*) (Oxford: Clarendon Press, 1953), 52–66.

[2] Ibid., 64–6.

[3] Roger Bacon, *The Opus Majus*, trans. by Robert B. Burke (New York: Russell and Russell, 1962), vol. II, 615–16.

[4] See, for instance, A. C. Crombie, *Robert Grosseteste*, 204–10.

[5] Roger Bacon, *The Opus Majus*, II. 626–7.

[6] A. C. Crombie, *Robert Grosseteste*, 73–4.

[7] *Duns Scotus: Philosophical Writings*, trans. and ed. by Allan Wolter (Edinburgh: Thomas Nelson, 1962), 109.

[8] Ibid., 110–11.

[9] See, for instance, Julius R. Weinberg, *Abstraction, Relation and Induction* (Madison: The University of Wisconsin Press, 1965), 145–7.

[10] Roger Bacon, *The Opus Majus*, II. 587.

[11] See A. C. Crombie, *Robert Grosseteste*, 233–59; W. A. Wallace, *The Scientific Methodology of Theodoric of Freiberg* (Fribourg: Fribourg University Press, 1959).

[12] Roger Bacon, *The Opus Majus*, II. 611.

[13] A. C. Crombie, 'Grosseteste's Position in the History of Science', in *Robert Grosseteste*, ed. by D. A. Callus (Oxford: Clarendon Press, 1955), 118.

[14] Ibid., 118–19.

[15] Euclid, *Elements*, Book IX, Proposition 20.

[16] John Buridan, *Questions on the Eight Books of the Physics of Aristotle*, Book VIII, Question 12, reprinted in M. Clagett, *The Science of Mechanics in the Middle Ages* (Madison: University of Wisconsin Press, 1959), 533.

[17] A. C. Crombie, *Robert Grosseteste*, 119–24.

[18] William of Ockham, *Summulae in Phys.*, III. 5–7, in *Ockham Studies and Selections*, trans. and ed. by S. C. Tornay (La Salle, Ill.: Open Court Publishing Co., 1938), 170–1.

[19] *Duns Scotus: Philosophical Writings*, 106–9.

[20] Nicolaus of Autrecourt, 'Second Letter to Bernard of Arezzo', in *Medieval Philosophy*, ed. by H. Shapiro (New York: The Modern Library, 1964), 516–20.

[21] J. R. Weinberg, *Nicolaus of Autrecourt* (Princeton, N.J.: Princeton University Press, 1948), 69.

[22] Ibid., 96–7.

6
The Debate over Saving the Appearances

NICOLAUS COPERNICUS (1473–1543) received a sinecure as canon at Frauenburg through the efforts of his influential uncle, the Bishop of Ermland. As a consequence, Copernicus was able to spend several years studying at Italian universities, and to pursue his project of reforming mathematical planetary astronomy. In the *De revolutionibus* (1543), Copernicus revised Ptolemy's mathematical models by eliminating equant points and by taking the sun to be (roughly) the centre of planetary motions.

JOHANNES KEPLER (1571–1630) was born in the Swabian city of Weil. He was of delicate constitution, and passed an unhappy childhood. Kepler found relief in his studies and his Protestant faith. At the University of Tübingen, Michael Maestlin interested him in the Copernican astronomy. The sun-centred system appealed to Kepler on aesthetic and theological grounds, and he devoted his life to the discovery of the mathematical harmony according to which God must have created the universe.

In 1594 he accepted a position as teacher of mathematics in a Lutheran school at Graz. Two years later he published the *Mysterium Cosmo-*

graphicum, in which he stated his "nest of regular solids" theory of planetary distances. This work, like all his writings, displayed a Pythagorean
commitment informed by Christian fervour. In 1600, partly to escape
pressure from Catholics in Graz, Kepler went to Prague as assistant to
the great observational astronomer Tycho Brahe. He eventually gained
access to Tycho's observations, and for the most part tempered his
enthusiasm for mathematical correlations with respect for the accuracy
of Tycho's data. Kepler published the first two laws of planetary motion
in *Astronomia Nova* (1609), and the third law in *De Harmonice Mundi*
(1619).

OSIANDER ON MATHEMATICAL MODELS AND PHYSICAL TRUTH

THE question of proper method in astronomy was still debated in
the sixteenth century. The Lutheran theologian Andreas Osiander
affirmed the tradition of saving the appearances in his Preface to
Copernicus's *De revolutionibus*. Osiander argued that Copernicus was
working in the tradition of those astronomers who freely invent
mathematical models in order to predict the positions of the planets.
Osiander declared that it does not matter whether the planets really
do revolve around the sun. What counts is that Copernicus has been
able to save the appearances on this assumption. In a letter to
Copernicus, Osiander tried to persuade him to present his sun-
centred system as a mere hypothesis for which only mathematical
truth was claimed.

COPERNICUS'S PYTHAGOREAN COMMITMENT

Copernicus, however, did not subscribe to this approach to astronomy. As a committed Pythagorean, he sought mathematical harmonies in phenomena because he believed they were "really there".
Copernicus believed that his sun-centred system was more than a
computational device.

Copernicus recognized that the observed planetary motions could
be deduced with about the same degree of accuracy from his system,
or from Ptolemy's system. Hence he acknowledged that selection of
one of these competing models was based on considerations other
than successful fit. Copernicus argued for the superiority of his own
system by appealing to "conceptual integration" as a criterion of
acceptability. He contrasted his own unified model of the solar system with Ptolemy's collection of separate models, one for each planet.
He noted, moreover, that the sun-centred system explains the mag-

nitudes and frequencies of the retrograde motions of the planets. The sun-centred system implies, for instance, that Jupiter's retrograde motion is more pronounced than that of Saturn, and that the frequency with which retrogression occurs is greater for Saturn than for Jupiter.* By contrast, Ptolemy's Earth-centred system provides no explanation of these facts.[1]

Copernicus died before having a chance to respond to Osiander's Preface to his book. Consequently, the sixteenth-century confrontation of the two methodological orientations—Pythagoreanism and the concern to save appearances—was not as sharp as it might have been.

BELLARMINE v. GALILEO

It remained for Cardinal Bellarmine and Galileo to state the rival positions with maximum intensity. Bellarmine informed Galileo in 1615 that it was permissible, from the standpoint of the Church, to discuss the Copernican system as a mathematical model to save the appearances. He indicated, moreover, that it is permissible to judge that the Copernican model is better able to save the appearances than is the Ptolemaic model. But Bellarmine insisted that to judge one mathematical model superior to another is not the same thing as to demonstrate the physical truth of the assumptions of the model.

The Jesuit mathematician Christopher Clavius had declared (in 1581) that Copernicus had saved the appearances of planetary motions by deducing theorems about them from *false* axioms. Clavius held that there was nothing exceptional about Copernicus's achievement, for, given a true theorem, any number of sets of false premisses can be found which imply the theorem. Clavius himself preferred the Ptolemaic system, because he believed that an Earth-centred system is consistent with both the principles of physics and the teachings of the Church.

Bellarmine was aware that many influential churchmen shared the opinion of Clavius, and he warned Galileo that it would be dangerous to defend the position that the sun really is stationary, and that the Earth really does revolve around it.

Galileo, as is well known, overplayed his hand. Despite his disclaimers to the contrary, his *Dialogue Concerning the Two Great World Systems* was a thinly veiled polemic on behalf of the Copernican

---

* Assuming, of course, that the orbital velocities of the planets decrease regularly, proceeding outwards from Mercury to Saturn.

system. Galileo did not regard the heliocentric hypothesis as a mere computational device to save appearances. Indeed, he advanced a number of arguments in favour of the *physical truth* of the Copernican system. It was of great importance for the subsequent development of science that Galileo supplemented his Pythagorean commitment with the conviction that suitably chosen experiments can establish the existence of mathematical harmonies in the universe.

KEPLER'S PYTHAGOREAN COMMITMENT

The Pythagorean orientation yielded substantial dividends in the astronomical investigations of Johannes Kepler. Kepler believed it to be significant that there exist just six planets and just five regular solids. Because he believed that God created the solar system according to a mathematical pattern, he sought to correlate the distances of the planets from the sun with these geometrical figures. In the *Mysterium Cosmographicum*, a book published in 1596, he announced with some pride that he had succeeded in gaining insight into God's

Kepler's Nest of Regular Solids

plan of creation. Kepler showed that the distances of the planets can be correlated with the radii of spherical shells, which are inscribed within, and circumscribed around, a nest of the five regular solids. Kepler's arrangement was:

Sphere of Saturn
Cube
Sphere of Jupiter
Tetrahedron
Sphere of Mars
Dodecahedron
Sphere of Earth
Icosahedron
Sphere of Venus
Octahedron
Sphere of Mercury

Kepler was able to achieve a rough agreement between the observed ratios of the radii of the planets and ratios calculated from the geometry of the nest of regular solids. However, he took values of planetary radii from data of Copernicus, which referred planetary distances to the centre of the Earth's orbit. Kepler hoped to improve the rough correlation achieved by his theory by referring planetary distances to the sun, thereby taking account of the eccentricity of the Earth's orbit. He recomputed the ratios of the planetary radii on this basis, using Tycho Brahe's more accurate data, and found that these ratios differed substantially from the ratios calculated from the regular-solid theory. Kepler accepted this as a refutation of his theory, but his Pythagorean faith was unshaken. He was convinced that the discrepancies between observation and theory themselves must be a manifestation of yet-to-be-discovered mathematical harmonies.

Kepler persevered in the search for mathematical regularities in the solar system, and eventually succeeded in formulating three laws of planetary motion:

(1) The orbit of a planet is an ellipse with the sun at one focus.

(2) The radius vector from the sun to a planet sweeps over equal areas in equal times.

(3) The ratio of the periods of any two planets is directly proportional to the ratio of the cubes of their mean distances from the sun.

Kepler's discovery of the Third Law is a striking application of Pythagorean principles. He was convinced that there must be a mathematical correlation between planetary distances and orbital velocities. He discovered the Third Law only after having tried a number of possible algebraic relations.

The committed Pythagorean believes that if a mathematical relation fits phenomena, this can hardly be a coincidence. But Kepler, in particular, formulated a number of mathematical correlations whose status is suspect. For example, he correlated planetary distances and their "densities". He suggested that the densities of the planets are inversely proportional to the square roots of their distances from the sun. Kepler had no way to determine independently the densities of the planets. In spite of this, he noted that the densities calculated from this mathematical relation could be correlated with the densities of well-known terrestrial substances. He set up the following table:[2]

Kepler's Distance—Density Relation

Planet	$Density = 1\sqrt{distance}$ (Earth = 1,000)	Terrestrial substance
Saturn	324	The hardest precious stones
Jupiter	438	The lodestone
Mars	810	Iron
Earth	1,000	Silver
Venus	1,175	Lead
Mercury	1,605	Quicksilver

Kepler noted with satisfaction that it would be appropriate to correlate the sun with gold, the density of which is greater than that of quicksilver. Of course, Kepler did not believe that the Earth was composed of silver and Venus of lead, but he did believe it important that his calculated planetary densities correspond to the densities of these terrestrial substances.

From the Pythagorean standpoint, the adequacy of a mathematical correlation is determined by appeal to the criteria of "successful fit" and "simplicity". Provided that a relation is not unduly complex mathematically, if it fits the phenomena under consideration, it must be important. But a person who does not share the Pythagorean faith doubtless would judge Kepler's distance-density correlation to be a coincidence. Such a person might appeal to criteria other than successful fit and simplicity, on the grounds that application of these criteria alone is not sufficient to distinguish genuine correlations from coincidental correlations.

BODE'S LAW

The evaluation of mathematical correlations has been a continuing problem in the history of science. In 1772, for example, Johann Titius suggested a correlation that was in the Pythagorean tradition. He noted that the distances of the planets from the sun could be correlated with the "suitably adjusted" terms of the geometrical series 3, 6, 12, 24. . ., viz.:

Bode's Law

4 0	4 3	4 6	4 12	4 24
Calculated 4	7	10	16	28
Planet Mercury	Venus	Earth	Mars	(Asteroids)
Observed 3.9	7.2	10	15.2	

4 48	4 96	4 192	4 384	
Calculated 52	100	196	388	
Planet Jupiter	Saturn	(Uranus)	(Neptune)	(Pluto)
Observed 52.0	95.4	191.9	300.7	395

The numbers thus obtained are in striking agreement with the observed distances, relative to Earth = 10. The noted astronomer Johann Bode was greatly impressed by this relation. He accepted the Pythagorean position that a successful fit is not likely to be a coincidence. Because he championed this relation, it came to be known as 'Bode's Law'. In 1780, an astronomer's judgement of the significance of Bode's Law was a good measure of the strength of his commitment to the Pythagorean orientation.

Then, in 1781, William Herschel discovered a planet beyond Saturn. Astronomers on the continent calculated the distance of Uranus from the sun and found it to be in excellent agreement with the next term in Bode's Law (196). Eyebrows were raised. The sceptics no longer could dismiss this correlation as an "after the fact" numerical coincidence. An increasing number of astronomers began to take Bode's Law seriously. A search was undertaken for the "missing planet" between Mars and Jupiter, and the asteroids Ceres and Pallas were discovered in 1801 and 1802. Although the asteroids were much smaller than Mercury, their distances were such that astronomers who believed in Bode's Law were satisfied that the missing term in the series had been filled.

After it became apparent that the motion of Uranus was being affected by a still more distant planet, J. C. Adams and U. J. J. Leverrier independently calculated the position of this new planet. One ingredient in their calculations was the assumption that the mean distance of the new planet would be given by the next term in Bode's Law (388). The planet Neptune was discovered by Galle in the region predicted by Leverrier. However, continued observation of the planet revealed that its mean distance from the sun (relative to Earth = 10) is about 300, which is not in good agreement with Bode's Law.*

With the inclusion of Neptune, Bode's Law no longer satisfied the criterion of successful fit. Hence one may be a Pythagorean today without being impressed by Bode's Law. On the other hand, since Pluto's distance is very close to the Bode's Law value for the next planet beyond Uranus, a person with a Pythagorean bent might be tempted to explain away the anomalous case of Neptune by insisting that Neptune is lately captured acquisition of the solar system, and not one of the original planets at all.

REFERENCES

[1] Copernicus, *On the Revolutions of the Heavenly Spheres*, Bk. I, Chap. 10.
[2] Kepler, *Epitome of Copernican Astronomy*, trans. by C. G. Wallis, in *Ptolemy, Copernicus, Kepler*—Great Books of the Western World, vol. 16 (Chicago, Ill.: Encyclopaedia Britannica, Inc. 1952), 882.

* Neptune's position in its orbit at the time of discovery was such that the over-estimation of its distance from the sun did not greatly affect the accuracy of the prediction of its position against the background stars.

7
The Seventeenth-Century Attack on Aristotelian Philosophy

I. Galileo

GALILEO GALILEI (1564–1642) was born at Pisa of noble but impoverished parents. In 1581 he enrolled at the University of Pisa to pursue the study of medicine, but soon abandoned his medical studies in favour of mathematics and physics.

In 1592 he was appointed Professor of Mathematics at the University of Padua, where he remained until 1610. During this period, Galileo made important telescopic observations of sunspots, the surface of the moon, and four of the satellites of Jupiter. These observations were inconsistent with implications of the Church-sanctioned Aristotelian world-view, in which the celestial realm is immutable and the Earth is the centre of all motion.

Galileo became mathematician-in-residence to the Grand Duke of Tuscany in 1610. He engaged in a series of disputes with Jesuit and Dominican philosophers, at one point lecturing these worthies on the proper way to interpret the Scriptures so as to effect agreement with the Copernican astronomy (*Letter to the Grand Duchess Christina*, 1615).

Galileo's admirer Maffeo Barberini was elected pope in 1623, and Galileo sought and received permission to prepare an impartial study of the rival Copernican and Ptolemaic systems. The *Dialogue Concerning the Two Chief World Systems* (1632) contained a preface and conclusion which indicated that the rival systems are mere mathematical hypotheses to save the appearances. The remainder of the book, which Galileo wrote in Italian to reach a wider audience, contained numerous arguments for the physical truth of the Copernican alternative.

Galileo was called before the Inquisition and forced to abjure his errors. He retired to Florence under the watchful eyes of his enemies. However, he gained revenge with the publication of the *Dialogues Concerning Two New Sciences* (1638), which demonstrated the inadequacy of Aristotle's physics, thereby removing a major support of geocentrism.

THE PYTHAGOREAN ORIENTATION AND THE DEMARCATION OF PHYSICS

GALILEO was convinced that the book of nature is written in the language of mathematics. For this reason, he sought to restrict the scope of physics to assertions about "primary qualities". Primary qualities are those qualities that undergo systematic quantitative variation relative to a scale. Galileo believed that primary qualities such as shape, size, number, position, and "quantity of motion", are objective properties of bodies, and that secondary qualities, such as colours, tastes, odours, and sounds, exist only in the mind of the perceiving subject.[1]

By restricting the subject-matter of physics to primary qualities and their relations, Galileo excluded teleological explanations from the range of permissible discourse of physics. According to Galileo, it is not a *bona fide* scientific explanation to state that a motion takes place *in order that* some future state may be realized. In particular, he urged that Aristotelian interpretations in terms of "natural motions" towards "natural places" do not qualify as scientific explanations. Galileo realized that he could not prove false an assertion such as "unsupported bodies move toward the Earth in order to reach their 'natural place'." But he also realized that this type of interpretation can be excluded from physics because it fails to "explain" the phenomena.

Implicit in Galileo's analysis is a distinction between two stages in the evaluation of interpretations in science. The first stage is to demarcate scientific interpretations from non-scientific interpretations. Galileo agreed with Aristotle that this is a question of circumscribing the proper subject-matter of science. The second stage is to determine the acceptability of those interpretations that do qualify as scientific. Galileo's approach to the problem of evaluating interpretations in science may be represented as follows:

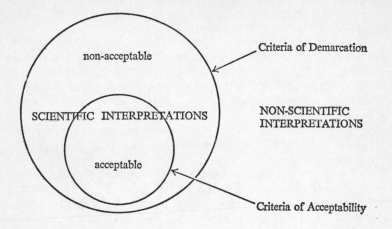

Galileo established the circumference of the larger circle by restricting the subject-matter of physics to statements about primary qualities.

One consequence of Galileo's demarcation of physics is that the motions of bodies are described with respect to a system of coordinates in space. Galileo replaced Aristotle's qualitatively differentiated space by a quantitatively differentiated geometrical space.

But his break with the qualitatively differentiated space of the Aristotelian universe was never complete. In the early work *le Motu*, Galileo himself affirmed the doctrine of "natural places".[2] Although subsequently he sought to exclude interpretations in terms of "natural places" from physics, he remained committed throughout his life to the doctrine that only circular motion is suited to celestial bodies. Galileo believed that the Earth itself is a *bona fide* celestial body, and he attempted to prove to the Aristotelians that the Earth, and bodies on its surface, participate in the perfection of circular motion. For example, he maintained that, in the absence of all resistance, motion along the Earth's surface would persist undiminished indefinitely.[3] In this instance, Galileo was guilty of formulating the same type of interpretation that his demarcation of physics was intended to exclude.

THEORY OF SCIENTIFIC PROCEDURE

Galileo's anti-Aristotelian polemic was *not* directed against Aristotle's inductive-deductive method. He accepted Aristotle's view of scientific inquiry as a two-stage progression from observations to general principles and back to observations.

Moreover, Galileo approved Aristotle's position that explanatory principles must be induced from the data of sense experience. In this regard, Galileo observed that Aristotle himself would have repudiated the doctrine of the immutability of the heavens had he been in possession of the seventeenth-century telescopic evidence on sunspots. He declared that "it is better Aristotelian philosophy to say 'Heaven is alterable because my senses tell me so', than to say 'Heaven is inalterable because Aristotle was so persuaded by reasoning.' "4

Galileo's remarks about scientific procedure were directed against practitioners of a false Aristotelianism, who short-circuited the Method of Resolution and Composition by beginning, not with induction from sense experience, but with Aristotle's own first principles. This false Aristotelianism encouraged a dogmatic theorizing which cut off science from its empirical base. Galileo frequently condemned this perversion of Aristotle's methodology.

The Method of Resolution

Galileo insisted on the importance to physics of abstraction and idealization, thereby extending the reach of inductive techniques. In his own work, he made use of idealizations such as 'free fall in a vacuum' and the 'ideal pendulum'. These idealizations are not exemplified directly in phenomena. They are formulated by extrapolating from serially ordered phenomena. The concept free fall in a vacuum, for example, is an extrapolation from the observed behaviour of bodies dropped in a series of fluids of decreasing density.5 The concept ideal pendulum is likewise an idealization. An "ideal" pendulum is one whose bob is attached to a "mass-less" string in which there are no frictional forces due to different periods of motion for different segments of the string. Moreover, the motion of such a pendulum is unimpeded by air resistance.

Galileo's work in mechanics testifies to the fertility of these concepts. He was able to deduce the approximate behaviour of falling bodies and real pendulums from explanatory principles that specify properties of idealized motions. One important consequence of this use of idealizations was to emphasize the role of creative imagination in the Method of Resolution. Hypotheses about idealizations can be obtained neither by induction by simple enumeration nor by the methods of agreement and difference. It is necessary for the scientist to intuit which properties of phenomena are the proper basis for idealization, and which properties may be ignored.[6]

The Method of Composition

Grosseteste and Roger Bacon had augmented the Method of Composition by suggesting the deduction of consequences not included in the data initially used to induce explanatory principles. Galileo made a striking application of this procedure by deducing from his hypothesis of the parabolic trajectory of projectiles, that the maximum range is achieved at 45 degrees. That the maximum range is achieved at 45 degrees was known prior to Galileo's work. Galileo's achievement was an explanation of this fact. Galileo also deduced from the parabolic trajectory that the same range is achieved for angles of elevation equally far removed from 45 degrees, e.g. 40 degrees and 50 degrees. He claimed that this had not been recognized by gunners, and used this occasion to eulogize the superiority of mathematical demonstration over untutored experience.[7]

Experimental Confirmation

Grosseteste and Roger Bacon had appended to the Method of Resolution and Composition a third stage in which the conclusions reached are further tested experimentally. Galileo's attitude toward this third stage has received very different evaluations. He has been hailed as a champion of experimental methodology. But he also has been criticized for failing to appreciate the importance of experimental confirmation. A case can be made for each evaluation, both from his comments on scientific procedure and from his scientific practice.

Galileo made ambivalent pronouncements on the value of experimental confirmation. His dominant emphasis is affirmative. For example, in the *Dialogues Concerning Two New Sciences,* after Salviati had deduced the law of falling bodies, Simplicio demanded experimental confirmation of this relation. Galileo had Salviati reply that "the request that you, as a man of science, make, is a very reasonable one; for this is the custom—and properly so—in those sciences where mathematical demonstrations are applied to natural phenomena."[8]

However, it is also true that Galileo occasionally wrote as if experimental confirmation were relatively unimportant. For example, after having deduced the variation of range of a projectile with the angle of elevation, he wrote that "the knowledge of a single fact acquired through a discovery of its causes prepares the mind to understand and ascertain other facts without need of recourse to experiment."[9]

A similar ambivalence over experimentation is found in Galileo's scientific practice. Very often he described experiments which he probably had performed himself.

From the standpoint of the history of physics, Galileo's most important experiments were on the problem of falling bodies. Galieo reported that he had confirmed the law of falling bodies by rolling balls down inclined planes of various heights. Although he did not state the values obtained in these experiments, he did go into considerable detail about the construction of the planes and the measurement of the time of fall by a water clock.[10]

Galileo also reported that he had performed experiments with a pendulum to confirm the hypothesis that the speeds achieved by a body moving down planes of different inclinations are equal when the heights of the planes are equal. He claimed that if the motion of a pendulum, consisting of a bullet tied to a string, is arrested when the string strikes a nail, then the bullet reaches the same height as it did when its oscillation was unimpeded.

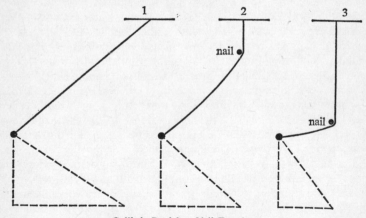

Galileo's Pendulum-Nail Experiment

Galileo maintained that the pendulum-nail experiment indirectly confirmed the hypothesis about motion on inclined planes. He noted that a direct confirmation by rolling a ball down one plane and up a second is impractical because of the "obstacle" at the point of junction.[11]

Galileo's less widely publicized experiments include a demonstration that a floating hollow wooden vessel does not sink when the cavity is filled with water,[12] and an occultation of stars by a rope to show that stellar diameters are exaggerated by the naked eye.[13]

In spite of his descriptions of experiments supposedly performed, however, Galileo's commitment to experimental confirmation was not complete. There are instances in which he dismissed experimental evidence that seemed to count against his theories.

In the early work *de motu*, for example, Galileo formulated the relationship $\frac{v_1}{v_2} = \frac{d_1 - d_m}{d_2 - d_m}$, in which v_1 and v_2 are the velocities of fall of two spheres of equal volume through a medium, d_1 and d_2 are the densities of these bodies, and d_m is the density of the medium. Commenting on this relationship, he admitted that if one drops from a tower two balls, chosen so that $\frac{d_1 - d_m}{d_2 - d_m} = 2$, a corresponding ratio in velocities is *not* observed. Indeed, the two balls hit the ground at approximately the same time. Galileo attributed this failure in confirmation to "unnatural accidents".[14] In this instance, he was anxious to recommend a mathematical relationship, which he believed followed from Archimedes' law of buoyancy, in spite of the fact that it does not describe the behaviour of bodies falling through air. Galileo subsequently abandoned this relationship in favour of a kinematic approach in which the distance of fall is related to the elapsed time.

Galileo also dismissed evidence that was unfavourable to his theory of the tides. He believed that the tides are caused by the periodic reinforcement and opposition of two motions of the Earth— its annual revolution around the sun and its daily rotation on its axis. Galileo's hypothesis, roughly put, was that for a given port P, revolution and rotation augment one another at midnight and oppose one another at noon.

The result of this periodic reinforcement and cancellation is that the water offshore is left behind at night and is piled up along the

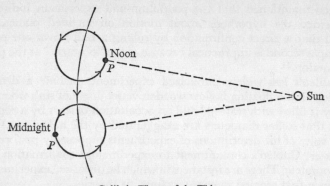

Galileo's Theory of the Tides

coast in the day-time. It follows from Galileo's theory that there should be just one high tide each day at a given location, and that it should occur around noon.

But it was a well-established fact that there are two high tides per day at a given port. Moreover, the times at which they occur vary around the clock from day to day. Galileo chose not to be deterred by these recalcitrant facts. He attributed the divergence of theory and fact to the operation of unimportant secondary causes, such as the irregular depth of the sea and the shape and orientation of the coast-line. Galileo was so anxious to find arguments for the motion of the Earth, that he was willing to dismiss evidence which counted against his theory of the tides.

In addition, there is one instance in which Galileo reported having confirmed a law for a range in which the law does not hold. He claimed to have observed that the period of a pendulum is independent of the amplitude of its swings for angles as high as 80 degrees from the perpendicular.[15] But the period of a pendulum is independent of its amplitude only for small displacements from the perpendicular. One must conclude either that Galileo did not bother to experiment with swings of large angle, or that his observations were extremely careless. Perhaps his error may be attributed to a strong conviction about how a pendulum *should* swing.

THE IDEAL OF DEDUCTIVE SYSTEMATIZATION

Galileo affirmed the Archimedean ideal of deductive systematiz-ation. And he also accepted the Platonic distinction between the real and the phenomenal, with which this ideal often was associated. From the standpoint of this distinction, it is natural to de-emphasize discrepancies between the theorems of deductive systems and what actually is observed. Such discrepancies may be attributed to "unimportant" experimental complications. As noted above, Galileo sometimes took recourse to this approach.

However, a more important aspect of Galileo's Archimedean-Platonic commitment was his emphasis on the value of abstraction and idealization in science. This was the converse side, as it were, of his willingness to explain away discrepancies between theory and observation. It was stressed above that much of Galileo's success in physics may be attributed to his ability to bracket out various empirical complications in order to work with ideal concepts such as "free fall in a vacuum", "ideal pendulum", and the "frictionless motion of a ship through the ocean". This is a positive feature of the ideal of deductive systematization. Galileo himself was quite sophisticated about the role of abstraction in science. He wrote that

just as the computer who wants his calculations to deal with sugar, silk, and wool must discount the boxes, bales, and other packings, so the mathematical scientist, when he wants to recognize in the concrete the effects which he has proved in the abstract, must deduct the material hindrances, and if he is able to do so, I assure you that things are in no less agreement than arithmetical computations. The errors, then, lie not in the abstractness or concreteness, not in geometry or physics, but in a calculator who does not know how to make a true accounting.[16]

REFERENCES

[1] Galileo, *The Assayer*, trans. by S. Drake, in *The Controversy on the Comets of 1618*, trans. by S. Drake and C. D. O'Malley (Philadelphia: University of Pennsylvania Press, 1960), 309.

[2] Galileo, *On Motion*, trans. by I. E. Drabkin, in Galileo, *On Motion and On Mechanics*, trans. by I. E. Drabkin and S. Drake (Madison: The University of Wisconsin Press, 1960), 14–16.

[3] Galileo, *Dialogue Concerning the Two Chief World Systems*, trans. by S. Drake (Berkeley: University of California Press, 1953), 148;

Dialogues Concerning Two New Sciences, trans. by H. Crew and A. de Salvio (New York: Dover Publications, 1914), 181–2;

"Second Letter from Galileo to Mark Welser on Sunspots", in *Discoveries and Opinions of Galileo*, trans. and ed. by S. Drake (Garden City, N.Y.: Doubleday Anchor Books, 1957), 113–14.

[4] Galileo, *Two World Systems*, 56.

[5] Galileo, *Two New Sciences*, 72.
[6] Galileo, *Two World Systems*, 207–8.
[7] Galileo, *Two New Sciences*, 276.
[8] Ibid., 178.
[9] Ibid., 276.
[10] Ibid., 178–9.
[11] Ibid., 172.
[12] Galileo, *Discourse on Bodies in Water*, trans. by T. Salusbury (Urbana: University of Illinois Press, 1960), 22.
[13] Galileo, *Two World Systems*, 361–4.
[14] Galileo, *On Motion*, 37–8.
[15] Galileo, *Two New Sciences*, 254–5, 85; *Two World Systems*, 450.
[16] Galileo *Two World Systems*, 207–8.

II Francis Bacon

FRANCIS BACON (1561–1626) was a son of Sir Nicholas Bacon, lord keeper to Queen Elizabeth I. Bacon entered Trinity College, Cambridge at the age of thirteen, and there developed an antipathy towards Aristotelian philosophy. Subsequently, he studied law at Gray's Inn and was admitted to the bar in 1586.

Bacon made numerous efforts to secure a governmental appointment from the Queen, but although his uncle William Cecil, later Lord Burghley, was Elizabeth's most important minister, the appointment was not forthcoming. This doubtless was due in part to Bacon's defence of the rights of Commons against certain proposals urged by the Queen's ministers.

Following the accession of James I, Bacon's fortunes soared. He became knighted in 1603, Attorney General in 1613, Lord Keeper in 1617, Lord Chancellor in 1618, Baron Verulam in 1618, and Viscount St.

Albans in 1621. Shortly thereafter, he pleaded guilty of taking gifts from persons with cases before him in his capacity as Lord Chancellor. Bacon insisted that he had not allowed the receipt of gifts to influence his judgements in these cases, but he offered no defence against the charge that he had accepted the gifts. Bacon was fined, jailed, and banished from public life by his peers in the House of Lords, but the King remitted the fine and terminated his imprisonment after a few days.

Bacon spent much of his time during the last five years of his life working on his *Great Instauration*, a proposed reformulation of the sciences. His most important contribution towards this Instauration was the *Novum Organum*, which he had published in 1620. In this work, he outlined a "new" scientific method to replace that of Aristotle. He also created an influential image of co-operative scientific inquiry in the *New Atlantis* (1627).

THE CONTROVERSY OVER THE VALUE OF BACON'S CONTRIBUTION

Francis Bacon is a controversial figure in the history of science. In the eyes of the founders of the Royal Society he was the prophet of a new scientific methodology. The *philosophes* likewise regarded Bacon to be an innovator, a champion of a new inductive–experimental method. But Alexandre Koyré and E. J. Dijksterhuis, two eminent twentieth-century historians, have minimized the value of Bacon's contributions. They have emphasized that Bacon achieved no new results in science, and that his criticism of Aristotelian method was neither original nor incisive. According to Dijksterhuis, Bacon's role in science was analogous to the military role of the lame Greek poet Tyrtaeus. Tyrtaeus could not fight, but his war-songs brought inspiration to those who could.[1]

The disputants agree about several aspects of Bacon's contribution: (1) that Bacon himself did not enrich science by means of concrete examples of his professed method; (2) that Bacon's great literary gifts enabled him to express his ideas so effectively that many scholars have attributed to him a large role in the scientific revolution of the seventeenth century; and (3) that Bacon's originality, if any, is his theory of scientific method.

Bacon himself claimed originality for his method. He chose as title of his principal work on method '*Novum Organum*', thereby indicating that his method was to replace the method discussed in the *Organon*, a medieval compilation of Aristotle's writings. Some critics have maintained that Bacon was successful. For instance,

John Herschel declared in his influential *Preliminary Discourse on Natural Philosophy* (1830) that

by the discoveries of Copernicus, Kepler, and Galileo, the errors of the Aristotelian philosophy were effectually overturned on a plain appeal to the facts of nature; but it remained to show on broad and general principles, how and why Aristotle was in the wrong; to set in evidence the peculiar weakness of his method of philosophizing, and to substitute in its place a stronger and better. This important task was executed by Francis Bacon.[2]

CRITICISM OF ARISTOTELIAN METHOD

But was Bacon's method a "new" *Organon*? Bacon insisted that the first requirement of scientific method is that the natural philosopher should purge himself of prejudices and predispositions in order to become again as a child before nature. He noted that the study of nature has been obscured by four classes of "Idols" which beset men's minds. Idols of the Tribe have their foundation in human nature itself. The understanding is prone to postulate more regularity in nature than it actually finds, to generalize hastily, and to over-emphasize the value of confirming instances. Idols of the Cave, by contrast, are attitudes towards experience that arise from the upbringing and education of men as individuals. Idols of the Market-Place are distortions that ensue when the meanings of words are reduced to the lowest common denominator of vulgar usage, thereby impeding scientific concept-formation. And Idols of the Theatre are the received dogmas and methods of the various philosophies.

Aristotle's philosophy was an Idol of the Theatre that Bacon was most anxious to discredit. It must be emphasized, however, that Bacon accepted the main outline of Aristotle's inductive–deductive theory of scientific procedure. Bacon, like Aristotle, viewed science as a progression from observations to general principles and back to observations. It is true that Bacon emphasized the inductive stage of scientific procedure. But he did assign to deductive arguments an important role in the confirmation of inductive generalizations.[3] Moreover, Bacon insisted that the fruits of scientific inquiry are new works and inventions, and noted that this is a matter of deducing from general principles consequences that have practical application.[4]

But although Bacon did accept Aristotle's theory of scientific procedure, he was highly critical of the way in which this procedure had been carried out. With respect to the inductive stage, Bacon issued a three-part indictment.

First, Aristotle and his followers practise a haphazard, uncritical collection of data. Francis Bacon called for a thorough-going implementation of Roger Bacon's Second Prerogative of Experimental Science, viz., the use of systematic experimentation to gain new knowledge of nature. In this connection, Francis Bacon stressed the value of scientific instruments in the collection of data.

Second, the Aristotelians generalize too hastily. Given a few observations, they leap at once to the most general principles, and then use these principles to deduce generalizations of lesser scope.

Third, Aristotle and his followers rely on induction by simple enumeration, in which correlations of properties found to hold for several individuals of a given type, are affirmed to hold for all individuals of that type. But application of this inductive technique often leads to false conclusions, because negative instances are not taken into account (Bacon did not mention the emphasis placed on a method of difference by such medieval writers as Grosseteste and Ockham).

With respect to the deductive stage of scientific inquiry, Bacon made two principal complaints. Bacon's first complaint was that the Aristotelians had failed to define adequately such important predicates as 'attraction', 'generation', 'element', 'heavy', and 'moist', thereby rendering useless those syllogistic arguments in which these predicates occur.[5] Bacon correctly pointed out that syllogistic demonstration from first principles is effective only if the terms of the syllogisms are well defined.

Bacon's second complaint was that Aristotle and his followers had reduced science to deductive logic by overemphasizing the deduction of consequences from first principles. Bacon stressed that deductive arguments are of scientific value only if their premisses have proper inductive support.

At this point, Bacon should have distinguished between Aristotle's theory of procedure and the way in which this theory of procedure had been misappropriated by some subsequent thinkers who called themselves "Aristotelians". Practitioners of a false Aristotelianism had short-circuited Aristotle's method by beginning, not with induction from observational evidence, but with Aristotle's own first principles. This false Aristotelianism encouraged a dogmatic theorizing by cutting off science from its empirical base. But Aristotle himself had insisted that first principles be induced from observational evidence. Bacon was unfair to condemn Aristotle for reducing science to deductive logic.

"CORRECTION" OF ARISTOTELIAN METHOD

Bacon put forward his "new" method for science in order to overcome the supposed deficiencies of the Aristotelian theory of procedure. The two principal features of Bacon's new method were an emphasis on gradual, progressive inductions, and a method of exclusion.

Bacon believed that properly conducted scientific inquiry is a step-by-step ascent from the base to the apex of a pyramid of propositions, viz.

Bacon's "Ladder of Axioms"

Bacon suggested that a series of "natural and experimental histories" should be compiled in order to establish a secure base for the pyramid. Bacon himself contributed works on the winds, the ebb and flow of the tides, and the longevity and modes of life of various peoples and animals. Unfortunately, he took much of the materials for his natural histories from untrustworthy sources.

Bacon held that, after having established the facts in a particular science, the natural philosopher should seek correlations within these facts. And he insisted on a gradual inductive ascent, from correlations of a low degree of generality to those which are more inclusive.

Bacon was aware that some correlations among facts are only "accidental" correlations. To weed out accidental correlations, he formulated a method of exclusion. Bacon suggested that accidental correlations often may be identified by inspecting Tables of Presence, Absence, and Degrees. Any correlation for which there is an instance in which one attribute is absent when another is present, or instances in which one attribute decreases when the other increases, is to be excluded from the pyramid. Bacon believed that after accidental correlations had been excluded in this way, only essential correlations would remain. And essential correlations are suitable subject-matter for further inductive generalization.

Bacon cited the method of exclusion as an important point of superiority of his method over that of Aristotle. He correctly maintained that simple enumeration, which was one of the inductive procedures employed by Aristotle, is inadequate to distinguish essential correlations from accidental correlations. Bacon claimed that application of the method of exclusion can effect this distinction, because this method places due weight on absence and relative intensity.

Bacon was sufficiently realistic to recognize that, in many cases, it is difficult to find essential correlations merely by inspecting Tables of Presence, Absence, and Degrees. For this reason, he singled out various types of "Prerogative Instances" which are of special value in the search for essential correlations. He seemed to have believed that it is of the very nature of these instances to reveal essential correlations.

Perhaps the most important of Bacon's 27 Prerogative Instances is the "Instance of the Fingerpost". An Instance of the Fingerpost is an instance that decides the issue between competing explanations. Bacon himself suggested a crucial instance of this type to decide between two hypotheses about the ebb and flow of the tides. The first hypothesis was that the tides are an advance and retreat of waters, on analogy to water rocked to-and-fro in a basin. The second hypothesis was that the tides are a periodic lifting and falling of waters. Bacon noted that the basin hypothesis would be falsified if it could be shown that the temporally coincident high tides on the shores of Spain and Florida were not accompanied by ebb tides elsewhere. He suggested that a study of tides on the coasts of Peru and China would settle the issue.[6]

Bacon recognized that an instance is "crucial" only if it is inconsistent with every set of explanatory premises save one. But it is not possible to prove that a statement about a type of phenomena can be deduced from just these several sets of premisses, and no others. Bacon was guilty of overestimating the logical force of Instances of the Fingerpost. Nevertheless, the elimination of hypotheses whose deductive consequences (given specific antecedent conditions), are not in agreement with observations, may be of value in the search for a more adequate explanation. Of course, Francis Bacon did not invent this method of falsification. Aristotle had employed it, and Grosseteste and Roger Bacon had recommended this method as a standard way to establish a hypothesis by eliminating competing hypotheses.

THE SEARCH FOR FORMS

Bacon referred to the most general principles at the apex of the pyramid as "Forms". Forms are the verbal expressions of relations among "simple natures", those irreducible qualities present in the objects we perceive. Bacon believed that various combinations of these simple natures constitute the objects of our experience, and that if we could but gain knowledge of Forms, it would be possible to control and modify the forces of nature.

In certain of his comments about Forms, Bacon seems to have conceived the union of simple natures in terms of an alchemical analogy. For instance, he declared that

he who knows the forms of yellow, weight, ductility, fixity, fluidity, solution, and so on, and the methods for superinducing them, and their gradations and modes, will make it his care to have them joined together in some body, whence may follow the transformation of that body into gold.[7]

Bacon himself contributed inquiries into the Forms of heat, whiteness, the attraction of bodies, weight, taste, memory, and the "Spirit enclosed within tangible bodies".[8]

Bacon's Forms are neither Platonic forms nor Aristotelian formal causes. Rather, Forms supposedly express those relations among physical properties that have the power to produce effects. In Aristotelian terms, Bacon's Forms refer to the material and efficient aspects of causation, as well as to the merely formal aspect.

In many cases (magnetism and the "Spirit enclosed within tangible bodies" are exceptions), Bacon specified Forms in terms of the configurations and motions of the invisible parts of bodies. He accepted the atomist principle that macroscopic effects are to be explained by submacroscopic interactions. But he did not accept the atomists' position that impact and impenetrability are the fundamental properties of atoms. Bacon attributed to the parts of bodies "forces" and "sympathies". Moreover, he did not accept the idea of a continuous void through which the atoms are dispersed.

Bacon placed two requirements on Forms: these propositions must be true in every instance, and the converses of these propositions must be true as well.* Bacon's Form of heat, for instance, states an identity of 'heat' and 'a rapid expansive motion of the small particles of bodies, which particles are restrained from escaping from the body's surface'.[10] According to Bacon, if heat is present, then so is this rapid expansive motion, and conversely. A similar convertibility supposedly holds for all Forms.

Bacon sometimes spoke of Forms as "laws". For example, in Book 2 of *Novum Organum*, he wrote that

when I speak of Forms, I mean nothing more than those laws and determinations of absolute actuality, which govern and constitute any simple nature, as heat, light, weight, in every kind of matter and subject that is susceptible of them. Thus the Form of Heat or the Form of Light is the same thing as the Law of Heat or the Law of Light.[11]

If extracted from context, certain of Bacon's remarks about "laws" have a modern ring. But several of Bacon's emphases are non-modern. In the first place, Bacon construed physical laws on the model of decrees enforced by a civil power. In the second place, Bacon was not interested in expressing laws in mathematical form. And in the third place, Bacon viewed the universe as a collection of substances which have properties and powers, and which stand in relations one to another. He did not view the universe as a flux of events which occur in lawful patterns. In this regard, Bacon's metaphysics is still Aristotelian.

One must conclude that Bacon's search for Forms is still very much in the Aristotelian tradition. John Herschel greatly overstated the case for the originality of Bacon's theory of procedure.

BACON AS PROPAGANDIST FOR ORGANIZED SCIENTIFIC RESEARCH

But if this were all there was to say about Bacon, it would be difficult to understand why he is a controversial figure in the history of

* These requirements correspond to Peter Ramus's Rules of Truth and Wisdom, respectively.[9]

science. It is true that Bacon sought to reform scientific method. However, there is more to Bacon's vision of science than his suggested "corrections" of Aristotle's theory of procedure.

Bacon accepted as a moral imperative that man is to recover the dominion over nature which he lost in the Fall. He repeatedly emphasized that men must control and redirect natural forces so as to improve the quality of life of their fellow human beings. Thus the discovery of Forms is only the proximate goal of scientific inquiry. One must gain knowledge of Forms before one can coerce nature to serve human purposes. But the ultimate goal of scientific inquiry is power over nature. Bacon's emphasis on the practical application of scientific knowledge stands in marked contrast to Aristotle's position that knowledge of nature is an end in itself. It is this emphasis on the control of natural forces that most clearly sets apart Bacon's philosophy from the Aristotelian philosophy he hoped to overthrow.

This emphasis on the practical application of scientific knowledge accounts for much of Bacon's excessively hostile polemics against Aristotle. Farrington is correct to point out that Bacon's hostility reflects *moral* outrage—Aristotle's philosophy not only has not led to new works to benefit mankind, but also has thwarted those few attempts that have been made.[12] By contrast, Bacon extolled the progress that had been made in the various craft traditions, and cited the inventions of printing, gunpowder, and the mariner's compass as examples of what can be accomplished by men not under the spell of Idols of the Theatre.

An important aspect of Bacon's new vision of science is that the recovery of man's dominion over nature is possible only through co-operative inquiry. In the service of this conviction, Bacon launched numerous attempts to introduce reforms administratively. He directed his appeals for support of co-operative projects almost exclusively to the Crown and its ministers, rather than to the universities, a strategy which reflected his very low estimate of contemporary academic life. But he was not successful. His vision of co-operative inquiry reached fruition only in the succeeding generation, when the Royal Society undertook to implement, not only Bacon's general attitude toward science, but also a number of Bacon's specific projects.

A further aspect of Bacon's new view of science is the divorce effected between science on the one hand, and teleology and natural theology on the other hand. Bacon restricted inquiry into final causes to the volitional aspects of human behaviour, observing that the search for final causes of physical and biological phenomena leads to purely verbal disputes which impede scientific progress.[13] Bacon's exclusion of final causes from natural science reflects his insistence that the scientist become again a child before nature. To view nature through the prism of purposive adaptation, whether divinely ordained or not, is to fail to come to grips with nature on its own terms. Preoccupation with the question "for what purpose?" makes unlikely the discovery of Forms and the subsequent improvement of the human condition.

REFERENCES

[1] E. J. Dijksterhuis, *The Mechanization of the World Picture*, trans. by C. Dikshoorn (Oxford: Clarendon Press, 1961), 402.

[2] John F. W. Herschel, *A Preliminary Discourse on the Study of Natural Philosophy* (London: Longman, Rees, Orme, Brown and Green, and John Taylor, 1831), 113–14.

[3] Francis Bacon, *Novum Organum, I*, Aphorism CVI.

[4] Ibid., *II*, Aphorism X.

[5] F. Bacon, 'Plan of the Work', in *The Works of Francis Bacon*, Vol. VIII, ed. by J. Spedding, R. L. Ellis, and D. D. Heath (New York: Hurd and Houghton, 1870), 41; *Novum Organum, I*, Aphorism XV.

[6] F. Bacon, *Novum Organum II*, Aphorism XXXVI.

[7] Ibid., *II*, Aphorism V.

[8] Ibid., *II*, Aphorisms XI–XXXVI.

[9] See Paolo Rossi, *Francis Bacon, From Magic to Science*, trans. by S. Rabinovitch (London: Routledge & Kegan Paul, 1968), 195–8.

[10] F. Bacon, *Novum Organum, II*, Aphorism XX.

[11] Ibid., *II*, Aphorism XVII.

[12] See Benjamin Farrington, *The Philosophy of Francis Bacon* (Liverpool: Liverpool University Press, 1964), 30.

[13] F. Bacon, *Novum Organum, II*, Aphorism II.

III. Descartes

RENÉ DESCARTES (1596–1650) attended the Jesuit College at La Flèche and received a law degree from the University of Poitiers in 1616. But because he shared in a considerable family fortune, it was not necessary for him to practise law. Descartes was very much interested in mathematics, science, and philosophy, and he decided to combine intellectual pursuits with travel. He spent several years travelling about Europe, frequently in the capacity of gentleman volunteer in various armies.

In 1618 Descartes made the acquaintance of the physicist Isaac Beeckman, who encouraged Descartes to undertake studies in theoretical mathematics. Descartes responded by laying the foundations of analytic geometry, in which the properties of geometrical surfaces are expressed by algebraic equations.

In November 1619, after a period of particularly intense intellectual effort, Descartes experienced three dreams, the interpretation of which greatly influenced his life. He believed that he had been called by the Spirit of Truth to reconstruct human knowledge in such a way that it should embody the certainty heretofore possessed only by mathematics.

Descartes established residence in Holland in 1628, and remained there, except for brief visits to France, until 1649. He prepared a treatise —*Le Monde*—which set forth a mechanistic interpretation of the universe within which all change is caused by impact or pressure. He withheld the manuscript, however, upon learning of Galileo's condemnation by the Inquisition. He decided to prepare the ground for acceptance of *Le Monde* through other publications. Among these were the *Discourse on Method* (1637), to which were appended treatises on geometry, optics, and meteorology, as examples of application of the method, *Meditations on First Philosophy* (1641), and *Principles of Philosophy* (1644). *Le Monde* itself was published posthumously in 1664.

In 1649 Descartes accepted an invitation to become philosopher-in-residence to Queen Christina of Sweden. He died the following year.

INVERSION OF FRANCIS BACON'S THEORY OF PROCEDURE

Descartes agreed with Francis Bacon that the highest achievement of science is a pyramid of propositions, with the most general principles at the apex. But whereas Bacon sought to discover general laws by progressive inductive ascent from less general relations, Descartes sought to begin at the apex and work as far downwards as possible by a deductive procedure. Descartes, unlike Bacon, was committed to the Archimedean ideal of a deductive hierarchy of propositions.

Descartes demanded certainty for the general principles at the apex of the pyramid. In the service of this demand for certainty, he undertook systematically to doubt all judgements which he previously had believed to be true, in order to see if any of these judgements were beyond doubt. He concluded that certain of his judgements were indeed beyond doubt—that in so far as he thinks, he must exist, and that there must exist a Perfect Being.

Descartes reasoned that a Perfect Being would not create man in such a way that his senses and reason should systematically deceive him. Thus there must exist a universe external to the thinking self, a universe not opaque to man's cognitive faculties. Indeed, Descartes went further than this, claiming that any idea which is both clearly and distinctly present to the mind must be true.

According to Descartes, the clear is that which is immediately present to the mind. The distinct, on the other hand, is that which is both clear and unconditioned. The distinct is known *per se;* its self-evidence is independent of any limiting conditions. For instance, I may have a clear idea of the "bentness" of a stick partially immersed in water, without understanding the factors responsible for the appearance of "bentness". But to achieve a distinct idea of the "bentness" of the stick, I would have to understand the law of refraction and the way it applies to this particular case.

PRIMARY QUALITIES AND SECONDARY QUALITIES

After having established his own existence as a thinking being, and the existence of a benevolent God who guarantees that what is clearly and distinctly present to the mind is true, Descartes turned his attention to the created universe. He sought to discover that which is clear and distinct about physical objects. Commenting on the melting of a lump of wax, he declared that

while I speak and approach the fire what remained of the taste is exhaled, the smell evaporates, the colour alters, the figure is destroyed, the size increases, it becomes liquid, it heats, scarcely can one handle it, and when one strikes it, no sound is emitted. Does the same wax remain after this change? We must confess that it remains; none would judge otherwise. What then did I know so distinctly in this piece of wax? It could certainly be nothing of all that the senses brought to my notice, since all these things which fall under taste, smell, sight, touch, and hearing, are found to be changed, and yet the same wax remains . . . abstracting from all that does not belong to the wax, let us see what remains. Certainly nothing remains excepting a certain extended thing which is flexible and movable.[1]

But how do we come to know this "extension" that constitutes the essence of the piece of wax? Descartes held that our knowledge of extension— the "real nature" of the wax—is an intuition of the mind. And this intuition of the mind is to be distinguished from the sequence of appearances that the wax presents to our senses. Descartes, like Galileo, distinguished between those "primary qualities" that all bodies must possess in order to be bodies, and the "secondary qualities"—colours, sounds, tastes, odours—that exist only in the perceptual experience of the subject.

Descartes reasoned that, since extension is the single property of bodies of which we have a clear and distinct idea, to be a body is to be extended. No vacuum can exist. Descartes took 'extension' to mean 'being filled by matter', and concluded that the concept "extension devoid of all matter" is a contradiction.[2]

But although he denied that a vacuum can exist in nature, Descartes did affirm certain of the methodological implications of classical atomism. He sought to interpret macroscopic processes in terms of submacroscopic interactions. An example is his interpretation of magnetic attraction. Descartes attributed the attraction of a magnet for a piece of iron to the emission from the magnet of invisible screw-shaped particles which pass through screwed channels present in the iron, thereby causing it to move. In addition, Descartes affirmed the atomist ideal of accounting for qualitative changes at the macroscopic level in terms of purely quantitative changes at the submacroscopic level. He restricted the subject-matter of science to those qualities that may be expressed in mathematical form and compared as ratios.

Descartes's vision of science thus combined the Archimedean, the Pythagorean, and the atomist points of view. For Descartes, the ideal of science is a deductive hierarchy of propositions, the descriptive terms of which refer to the strictly quantifiable aspects of reality, often at a submacroscopic level. No doubt he was influenced to accept this ideal by his early success in formulating analytic geometry. Descartes called for a universal mathematics to unlock the secrets of the universe, much as his analytic geometry had reduced the properties of geometrical surfaces to algebriac equations.

Unfortunately for this programme, Descartes also used the term 'extension' in a second sense. In order to describe the motions of bodies, he referred to bodies as occupying first one space and then another. For instance, if bodies A and B are bounded successively by bodies C and D, Descartes would speak of B as having moved into the "space" vacated by A.

But this "space" or "piece of extension", is not identical to any specific body. "Space", in this sense, is a relationship which a body has to other bodies. This dual usage of 'extension' is a serious equivocation. By Descartes's own standards, one must judge that he did not achieve a clear and distinct idea of "extension", his fundamental category for the interpretation of the universe.

THE GENERAL SCIENTIFIC LAWS

Be that as it may, Descartes proceeded to derive several important physical principles from his understanding of extension. Buchdahl has pointed out that Descartes seemed to believe that because the concepts extension and motion are clear and distinct, certain generalizations about these concepts are *a priori* truths.[3] One such generalization is that all motion is caused by impact or pressure. Descartes maintained that, since no vacuum can exist, a given body is continually in contact with other bodies. It seemed to him that the only way a body can be moved is if the adjacent bodies on one side exert a greater pressure than the adjacent bodies on the other side. By restricting the causes of motion to impact and pressure, he denied the possibility of action-at-a-distance. Descartes defended a thoroughly mechanistic view of causation.

Descartes's Mechanistic Philosophy was a revolutionary doctrine in the seventeenth century. Many thinkers who accepted it believed it to be more scientific than rival views which entertained such "occult" qualities as magnetic forces and gravitational forces. From the Cartesian standpoint, to say that a body moved towards a magnet because of some force exerted by the magnet is to explain nothing. One might as well say that the body moved towards the magnet because it desired to embrace it.

Another important physical principle derived from the idea of extension is that all motion is a cyclical rearrangement of bodies. Descartes reasoned that, if one body changes its "location", a simultaneous displacement of other bodies is necessary to prevent a vacuum. Moreover, it is only by moving along a closed loop that a finite number of bodies can alter their positions without creating a vacuum.

Descartes maintained that God is the ultimate cause of motion in the universe. He believed that a Perfect Being would create a universe "all at once".* Descartes concluded that, since the matter of the universe was set in motion all at once, a Perfect Being would ensure that this motion be conserved perpetually. Otherwise, the universe would resemble a clock that eventually runs down, the product of an all-too-human workman.

From this most general principle of motion, Descartes derived three other laws of motion:

Law I — Bodies at rest remain at rest, and bodies in motion remain in motion, unless acted upon by some other body.

Law II — Inertial motion is straight-line motion.†

Law III (A) — If a moving body collides with a second body, which second body has a greater resistance to motion than the first body has force to continue its own motion, then the first body changes its direction without losing any of its motion.

Law III (B) — If the first body has greater force than the second body has resistance, then the first body carries with it the second, losing as much of its motion as it gives up to the second.

* Descartes did not explain why a Perfect Being, of necessity, would opt for a single act of creation, rather than a continuing creation of matter and motion.

† And not, as Galileo had held, circular motion.

Descartes next deduced from these three laws seven rules of impact for specific kinds of collisions. These rules are incorrect, largely because Descartes took size, rather than weight, to be the determining factor in collisions. Of these rules of impact, the fourth is perhaps the most notorious. It states that, regardless of its speed, a moving body cannot budge a stationary body of greater size. In stating what he believed to be implied by the concepts "extension" and "motion," Descartes formulated a set of rules which are at variance with the observed motions of bodies.

Descartes claimed that the scientific laws he had elaborated were deductive consequences of his philosophical principles. In the *Discourse on Method* he wrote that

I have first tried to discover generally the principles or first causes of everything that is or that can be in the world, without considering anything that might accomplish this end but God Himself who has created the world, or deriving them from any source excepting from certain germs of truths which are naturally existent in our souls.[4]

Much of the appeal of the Cartesian philosophy derives from its breadth of scope. Beginning with theistic-creationist metaphysical principles, Descartes proceeded to derive the general laws of the universe. Descartes's version of the pyramid of scientific truths is depicted at the top of the following page.

EMPIRICAL EMPHASES IN DESCARTES'S PHILOSOPHY OF
SCIENCE

The Limitations of A Priori Deduction

Descartes realized that one could proceed by deduction only a short distance from the apex of the pyramid. Deduction from intuitively self-evident principles is of limited usefulness in science. It can yield only the most general of laws. Moreover, since the fundamental laws of motion only place limits on what can happen under certain types of circumstances, innumerable sequences of events are consistent with these laws. Broadly speaking, the universe we know is but one of the indefinitely many universes that could have been created in accordance with these laws.

Descartes pointed out that one cannot determine, from mere consideration of the general laws, the course of physical processes. The law of conservation of motion, for instance, stipulates that,

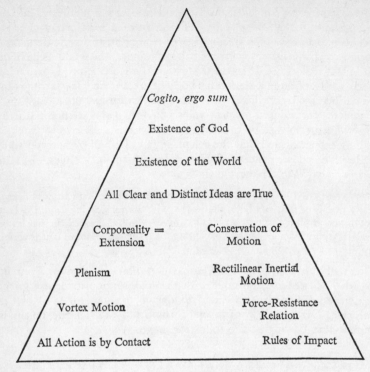

Descartes's Pyramid

whatever process is considered, no loss of motion is incurred. But just how motion is redistributed among the bodies involved must be determined for each type of process. In order to deduce a statement about a particular effect, it is necessary to include among the premisses information about the circumstances under which the effect occurred. In the case of the explanation of a physiological process, for example, the premisses must include specific information about anatomical structure, in addition to the general laws of motion. Thus one important role for observation and experiment in Descartes's theory of scientific method is to provide knowledge of the conditions under which events of a given type take place.

It is at this point that the Baconian programme of compiling natural histories and seeking correlations among phenomena is of value. Descartes conceded this much to Baconian science. He denied, however, that it is possible to establish important laws of nature by the collation and comparison of observed instances.

Role of Hypotheses in Science

A second important role of observation and experiment in Descartes's theory of scientific method is to suggest hypotheses which specify mechanisms that are consistent with the fundamental laws. Descartes held that a hypothesis is justified by its ability, in conjunction with the fundamental laws, to explain phenomena. The hypothesis must be consistent with the fundamental laws, but its specific content is to be adjusted to permit deduction of statements about the phenomena in question.

Frequently, Descartes suggested hypotheses that were based on analogies drawn from everyday experiences. He likened the motions of the planets to the revolution of bits of cork caught up in a whirlpool, the reflection of light to the bouncing of tennis balls on hard surfaces, and the action of the heart to the generation of heat in hay-mows. In each case the analogy to everyday experience was of crucial importance in the resultant theory.

It is quite likely that the use of pictorial analogies of this type contributed to the popularity of his theory of the universe. But more often than not, reliance on such analogies led Descartes astray.

A case in point is his explanation of the circulation of the blood. Descartes committed himself to an inappropriate analogy, and he ignored experimental evidence that counted against the analogy. According to Descartes, the heart, which generates heat on the model of spontaneous generation in hay-mows, vaporizes venous blood as it enters, thereby expanding the heart and propelling blood into the arterial system. Descartes's account conflicts with the facts. William Harvey had shown experimentally that the pulse of the blood into the arteries is accompanied by a *contraction* of the heart. Descartes had read Harvey's book on circulation, and had praised it, but elected to defend his own hypothesis nevertheless.[5]

Experimental Confirmation

It is on the issue of experimental confirmation that Descartes's theory of scientific method is most vulnerable. Clearly, he paid lip service, at least, to the value of experimental confirmation. He recognized, for instance, that a statement about a type of phenomena

may be deduced from more than one set of explanatory premisses
e.g.:

$$\frac{\begin{array}{c}\text{laws of nature}\\\text{statement of relevant circumstances}\\\text{hypothesis 1}\end{array}}{\therefore E}$$

$$\frac{\begin{array}{c}\text{laws of nature}\\\text{statement of relevant circumstances}\\\text{hypothesis 2}\end{array}}{\therefore E}$$

In such cases, Descartes specified that *other* effects be sought, such as
are deducible from premisses that include hypothesis 1, but are not
deducible from premisses that include hypothesis 2 (or vice versa).

However, Descartes's practice often did not match the sophistication of his writings about method. In general, he tended to regard
experimentation as an aid in formulating explanations rather than
as the touchstone of adequacy of such explanations.

Despite the fact that Descartes's interpretations often failed to
fit facts, his theory of the universe possessed great appeal. It accorded
due weight both to a desire for certainty and to an awareness of
the complexity of phenomena. The general laws of nature supposedly
were deductive consequences of necessary truths which must be
acknowledged by any reflective individual.* And if 'quantity of
motion' is interpreted as 'momentum', as Malebranche insisted, the
resulting rules of impact do not conflict with experience. But these
general laws explain phenomena only in conjunction with specific
factual information, and often, hypotheses. It was possible to remove

---

* Descartes was careful to emphasize that it was not necessary that God create
the universe in accordance with the laws of the pyramid. The laws are not a
constraint on God's creative activity. Indeed, Descartes held that it is within God's
power to have created a world in which contradictions are realized. For instance,
God could have created a world in which a circle has radii of different lengths,
and in which mountains are present without valleys.[6] Needless to say, this possibility is beyond *human* understanding.

Nevertheless, Descartes consistently maintained that the essence of natural
phenomena is extension and motion. And he often spoke as if the fundamental
laws of motion—for this world that God *did* create—could not be other than they
are. These laws are not mere empirical generalizations about what has been
observed. Rather, they state clearly and distinctly comprehended insights into
the structure of the universe.

discrepancies between theory and observation by altering the associated hypotheses, thus leaving intact the general laws of nature. The existence of this flexibility within the Cartesian system was one reason for its continuing popularity (suitably modified) during the seventeenth and eighteenth centuries.

REFERENCES

[1] René Descartes, *Meditations on First Philosophy*, in *The Philosophical Works of Descartes*, trans. and ed. by E. S. Haldane and G. R. T. Ross (New York: Dover Publications, 1955), vol. I, 154.

[2] Descartes, *The Principles of Philosophy*, Haldane and Ross, I, 260–3.

[3] Gerd Buchdahl, *Metaphysics and the Philosophy of Science* (Oxford: Blackwell, 1969), 125.

[4] Descartes, *Discourse on the Method of Rightly Conducting the Reason*, Haldane and Ross, I, 121.

[5] Ibid., I, 112.

[6] Descartes, 'Letter to Mersenne (May 27, 1630)', 'Letter for Arnauld (July 29, 1648)', in *Descartes—Philosophical Letters*, trans. and ed. by A. Kenny (Oxford Clarendon Press, 1970), 15, 236–7.

8
Newton's Axiomatic Method

ISAAC NEWTON (1642–1727) was born in Woolsthorpe (Lincolnshire). His yeoman father died before Isaac's birth. Newton's mother remarried when he was three, and his upbringing was relegated largely to a grandmother, until the death of his stepfather in 1653.

Newton attended Trinity College, Cambridge, and received a B.A. degree in 1665. During 1665–7, Newton stayed at Woolsthorpe to avoid the plague. This was a period of immense creativity, in which Newton formulated the binomial theorem, developed the "method of fluxions" (calculus), constructed the first reflecting telescope, and came to realize the *universal* nature of gravitational attraction.

Newton was appointed Professor of Mathematics at Cambridge in 1669, and was elected a fellow of the Royal Society in 1672. Shortly thereafter, he communicated to the Society his findings on the refractive properties of light. An extended debate ensued with Robert Hooke and others. The controversy with Hooke deepened upon publication of the *Mathematical Principles of Natural Philosophy* (1687). Hooke complained that Newton had appropriated his position that planetary motions could be explained by a rectilinear inertial principle in combination with a $1/r^2$

force emanating from the sun. Newton replied that he had come to this conclusion before Hooke, and that only he could prove that a $1/r^2$ force law leads to elliptical planetary orbits.

Newton became Warden of the Mint in 1696 and displayed considerable talent for administration. He was elected President of the Royal Society in 1703, and from this vantage-point carried on a running feud with Leibniz over priorities in the development of the calculus. In 1704, Newton published the *Opticks*, a model of experimental inquiry. He included in the "Queries" at the end of this book a statement of his view of scientific method.

Throughout his life Newton studied the Biblical records from the standpoint of a Unitarian commitment. Extensive notes on the chronology of ancient kingdoms and the exegesis of *Daniel* have been found among his papers.

THE METHOD OF ANALYSIS AND SYNTHESIS

Newton's comments about scientific method were directed primarily against Descartes and his followers. Descartes had sought to derive basic physical laws from metaphysical principles. Newton opposed this method of theorizing about nature. He insisted that the natural philosopher base his generalizations on a careful examination of phenomena. Newton declared that "although the arguing from Experiments and Observations by Induction be no Demonstration of general Conclusions, yet it is the best way of arguing which the Nature of Things admits of".[1]

Newton opposed the Cartesian method by affirming Aristotle's theory of scientific procedure. He referred to this inductive–deductive procedure as the "Method of Analysis and Synthesis". By insisting that scientific procedure should include both an inductive stage and a deductive stage, Newton affirmed a position that had been defended by Grosseteste and Roger Bacon in the thirteenth century, as well as by Galileo and Francis Bacon at the beginning of the seventeenth century.

Newton's discussion of the inductive–deductive procedure was superior to that of his predecessors in two respects. He consistently stressed the need of experimental confirmation of the consequences deduced by Synthesis, and he emphasized the value of deducing consequences that go beyond the original inductive evidence.

Newton's application of the Method of Analysis and Synthesis reached fruition in the investigations of the *Opticks*. For example, in a deservedly famous experiment, Newton passed a ray of sunlight through a prism such that an elongated spectrum of colour was produced on the far wall of a darkened room.

Newton's One-Prism Experiment

Newton applied the Method of Analysis to induce the explanatory principle that sunlight comprises rays of differing colours, and that each colour is refracted by the prism through a characteristic angle. This was not a simple inductive generalization on Newton's part. Newton did not affirm merely that all prisms under similar circumstances would produce spectra similar to those he had observed. His more important conclusion was about the nature of light itself, and it required an "inductive leap" to conclude that sunlight is made up of rays which have different refractive properties. After all, other interpretations of the evidence are possible. Newton might have concluded, for instance, that sunlight is indivisible, and that the spectral colours are produced instead by some sort of secondary radiation within the prism.

Given the "theory" that sunlight does comprise rays of different colours and refractive properties, Newton then applied the Method of Synthesis to deduce certain further consequences of the theory. He noted that if his theory were correct, then passing light of a particular colour through a prism should result in a deflection of the beam through the angle characteristic of that colour, but no resolution of the beam into other colours. Newton confirmed this consequence of his theory of colours by passing light from one small band of the spectrum through a second prism.[2]

Inductive Generalization and the Laws of Motion

Newton also claimed to have followed the Method of Analysis and Synthesis in his great work on dynamics, the *Mathematical Principles*

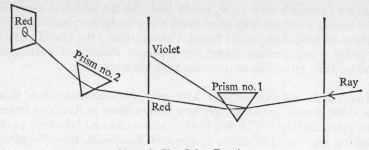

Newton's Two-Prism Experiment

of Natural Philosophy (1686). In this volume, he reported that he had formulated the three laws of motion upon application of the Method of Analysis. Newton declared that in experimental philosophy "particular propositions are inferred from the phenomena, and afterwards rendered general by induction. Thus it was that the impenetrability, the mobility, and the impulsive force of bodies, and the laws of motion and of gravitation, were discovered."[3]

Newton did not discuss the nature of the inductive process which proceeds from phenomena to particular propositions to the laws of motion. Whether or not it is correct to say that the laws of motion were discovered upon application of the Method of Analysis depends on how broadly one construes "induction".

Aristotle, for instance, admitted intuitive insight as a *bona fide* inductive method. Aristotle's theory of procedure thus could account for generalizations about weightless, infinitely rigid levers, ideal pendulums, and inertial motion. Indeed, it would be difficult to find a scientific interpretation whose origin could not be attributed to intuitive insight.

Most natural philosophers, however, have taken a more restricted view of induction, limiting it to a small number of techniques for generalizing the results of observation. These techniques include simple enumeration, and the methods of agreement and difference.

It is clear that Newton's Laws were not discovered upon application of these inductive techniques. Consider the first law. It specifies the behaviour of those bodies which are under the influence of no impressed forces. But no such bodies exist. And even if such a body did exist, we could have no knowledge of it. Observation of a body requires the presence of an observer or some recording apparatus.

But on Newton's own view, every body in the universe exerts a gravitational attractive force on every other body. An observed body cannot be free of impressed forces. Consequently, the law of inertia is not a generalization about the observed motions of particular bodies. It is, rather, an abstraction from such motions.

Absolute Space and Absolute Time. Moreover, Newton maintained that the three laws of motion specify how bodies move in Absolute Space and Absolute Time. This is a further abstraction on Newton's part. Newton contrasted Absolute Space and Time with their "sensible measures" which are determined experimentally.

Newton's distinction between the "true motions" of bodies in Absolute Space and Time and the "sensible measures" of these motions has a Platonic ring that suggests a dichotomy of reality and appearance. On Newton's view, Absolute Space and Absolute Time are ontologically prior to individual substances and their interactions. He believed, moreover, that an understanding of sensible motions can be achieved in terms of true motions in Absolute Space.

Newton recognised that to establish that a sensible measure of a body's motion is its true motion, or that a sensible motion is related in some specific way to its true motion, it would be necessary to specify both Absolute temporal intervals and coordinates in Absolute Space. But he was not certain that these requirements can be met.

With respect to Absolute Time, Newton declared that "it may be, that there is no such thing as an equable motion, whereby time may be accurately measured. All motions may be accelerated and retarded, but the flowing of absolute time is not liable to any change."[4] However, Newton did indicate that some sensible measures of time are preferable to others. He suggested that for the definition of temporal intervals, the eclipses of Jupiter's moons and the vibrations of pendulums are superior to the apparent motion of the sun around the Earth.[5]

But even if Absolute Time could be measured, it still would be necessary to locate a body in Absolute Space before its absolute motion could be determined. Newton was convinced that Absolute Space must exist, and he advanced both theological arguments and physical arguments for its existence, but he was less certain that bodies could be located in this space.

Newton maintained on theological grounds that since the universe was created *ex nihilo*, there must exist a receptacle within which created matter is distributed. He suggested that Absolute Space is an "emanent effect" of the Creator, a "disposition of all being" which is neither an attribute of God nor a substance coeternal with God. Newton criticized Descartes's identification of extension and body as offering a path to atheism, since, according to Descartes, we can achieve a clear and distinct idea of extension independently of its nature as a creation of God.[6]

The most important of Newton's physical arguments for the existence of Absolute Space was his analysis of the motion of a rotating, water-filled bucket. He noted that if such a bucket were suspended from a twisted rope and allowed to rotate as the rope unwinds, the water surface remains a plane for a time and only gradually assumes a concave shape. At length the water rotates at the same rate as the bucket. Newton's experiment showed that the deformation of the water surface could not be correlated with an acceleration of the water relative to the bucket, since the water surface is successively a plane and concave when there is a relative acceleration, and since the water surface may be either a plane or concave when there is no relative acceleration.

Newtons's Bucket Experiment

Event	Acceleration of Water relative to bucket in Earth-centred co-ordinate system	Surface of water
No. 1—bucket stationary	no	plane
No. 2—bucket released	yes	plane
No. 3—at maximum rotation	no	concave
No. 4—bucket arrested	yes	concave
No. 5—water at rest	no	plane

Newton maintained that deformation of the water surface indicates that a force is acting. And the second law of motion associates force and acceleration. But this acceleration of the water is an acceleration with respect to what? Newton concluded that since the acceleration associated with deformation is not an acceleration relative to the bucket, it must be an acceleration with respect to Absolute Space.[7]

Subsequently, numerous writers have pointed out that Newton's conclusion does not follow from his experimental findings. Ernst Mach, for example, suggested that the deformation be correlated, not with an acceleration with respect to Absolute Space, but with an acceleration with respect to the fixed stars. [8]

However, even if Newton were correct to conclude that the bucket experiment demonstrates the existence of an absolute motion, this would not suffice to specify a system of co-ordinates for locating positions in Absolute Space. Newton conceded this. Moreover, he admitted that there may be no single body which is at rest with respect to Absolute Space, and which may serve as a reference point for measuring distances in this space. [9]

Newton thus admitted that it may not be possible to achieve a wholly satisfactory correspondence between observed motions and true motions in Absolute Space. His explicit discussion of this problem of correspondence indicates that he followed an axiomatic method in the *Principia* rather than the inductive method of Analysis.

AN AXIOMATIC METHOD

There are three stages in Newton's axiomatic method. The first stage is the formulation of an axiom system. On Newton's view, an axiom system is a deductively organized group of axioms, definitions, and theorems. Axioms are propositions that cannot be deduced from other propositions within the system, and theorems are the deductive consequences of these axioms. The three laws of motion are the axioms of Newton's theory of mechanics. They stipulate invariant relations among such terms as 'uniform motion in a right line', 'change of motion', 'impressed force', 'action', and 'reaction'. The axioms are:

I. Every body continues in its state of rest, or of uniform motion in a right line, unless it is compelled to change that state by forces impressed upon it.

II. The change of motion is proportional to the motive force impressed; and is made in the direction of the right line in which that force is impressed.

III. To every action there is always opposed an equal reaction: or, the mutual actions of two bodies upon each other are always equal, and directed to contrary parts. [10]

Newton clearly distinguished the "absolute magnitudes" which appear in the axioms from their "sensible measures" which are determined experimentally. The axioms are *mathematical principles* of natural philosophy which describe the true motions of bodies in Absolute Space.

The second stage of the axiomatic method is to specify a procedure for correlating theorems of the axiom system with observations. Newton usually required that axiom systems be linked to events in the physical world.

However, he did submit for consideration a Theory of Colour-Mixing in which the axiom system was not properly linked to experience.[11] Newton specified that a circle be drawn and be subdivided into seven wedges—one for each of the "principal colours" of the spectrum—such that the widths of the wedges are proportional to the musical intervals in the octave. He further specified that the "number of rays" of each colour in the mixture be represented by a circle of greater or smaller radius located at the midpoint of the arc for each colour present in the mixture. Newton indicated that the centre of gravity of these circles gives the resultant colour of the mixture.

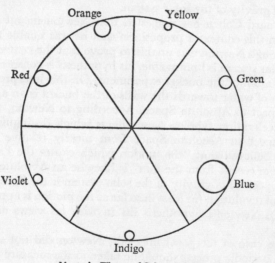

Newton's Theory of Colour-Mixing

Newton's axiom on slicing the pie to satisfy musical harmonies is reminiscent of Kepler's Pythagorean speculations. The axiom certainly is not an inductive generalization. Nevertheless, even though there is no evidence in support of the pie-slicing axiom, the theory would be useful if the results of mixing colours could be calculated from it. But Newton failed to provide an empirical interpretation for the phrase 'number of rays'. Since he did not stipulate how the diameters of the circles are to be determined, Newton's theory of colour-mixing has no empirical significance.

Newton's mechanics, on the other hand, does have empirical significance. He did link his axiom system for mechanics to events in the physical world. He achieved the required link by selecting "Rules of Correspondence" for the conversion of statements about Absolute spatial and temporal intervals into statements about measured spatial and temporal intervals.

In the case of spatial intervals, Newton asserted as a "hypothesis" that the centre of gravity of the solar system is immovable, and therefore a suitable reference point for the determination of Absolute distances. He thus was able to apply his axiom system to actual motions by selecting a co-ordinate system the origin of which is the centre of gravity of the solar system.

I. Bernard Cohen has suggested that Newton meant by "hypothesis" in this context a proposition that he was unable to prove.[12] But although Newton was unable to prove that the centre of gravity of the solar system is immovable, his hypothesis is consistent with his interpretation of the bucket experiment. On this interpretation, the recession of water towards the walls of the bucket is an acceleration with respect to Absolute Space. According to Newton, this centrifugal acceleration typifies those effects which distinguish motions with respect to Absolute Space from merely relative motions.[13] Newton believed that "the motion which causes the Earth to endeavour to recede from the Sun" is likewise an Absolute Motion.[14] Since the centre of gravity of the solar system is the "centre" of this motion of revolution (at least in so far as the motion is approximately circular), Newton's hypothesis fits in with his views on Absolute Motion.

In the case of temporal intervals, Newton did not specify that any one periodic process should be taken as the measure of Absolute Time. However, by reading between the lines, one can interpret Newton to have suggested a procedure to link Absolute Time with its sensible measures. Such a link might be established by examining time-dependent sequences which have been determined using various different methods of measuring time. For example, if the distance-time relationship for balls rolled down inclined planes is "more regular" when time is measured by the swings of a pendulum than when time is measured by the weight of water flowing through a hole in a pail, then the pendulum clock is the better "sensible measure" of Absolute Time.[15]

Newton thus carefully distinguished the abstract status of an axiom system from its application to experience. This distinction may be illustrated as follows:

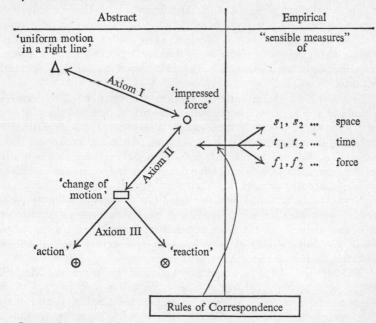

1. Centre of gravity of the solar system taken as the centre of Absolute Space.
2. Selection of the "best measure" of Absolute Time.
3. Moving bodies construed as systems of indefinitely large numbers of point-masses.
4. Specification of experimental procedures to measure values of impressed forces.

Newton's Interpreted Axiom System for Mechanics

Newton enforced the distinction between an axiom system and its application to experience throughout the *Principia*. In the section on fluid dynamics, for example, he distinguished "mathematical dynamics", in which motions are described under various hypothetical resistive conditions, from its application to experience. An application of mathematical dynamics is achieved after experimental determination of how the resistance of a specific medium varies with the velocity of a body moving through it. This distinction between an axiom system and its empirical application was one of Newton's most important contributions to the theory of scientific method. It raised to a new level of sophistication the ideal of the deductive systematization of scientific knowledge.

The third stage of Newton's axiomatic method is the confirmation of the deductive consequences of the empirically interpreted axiom system. Once a procedure is specified to link the terms of the axiom system to phenomena, the investigator must seek to establish agreement between the theorems of the axiom system and the observed motions of bodies.

Newton himself established extensive agreement between his empirically interpreted axiom system for mechanics and the motions of celestial and terrestrial bodies. An illustration is his experiments with colliding pendulums. Newton showed that after appropriate corrections are made for air resistance, action and reaction are equal regardless of whether the pendulum bobs are composed of steel, glass, cork, or wool.

Newton thus affirmed and practised *two* theories of scientific procedure—the Method of Analysis and Synthesis, and an Axiomatic Method. I think that it does not detract from Newton's genius to point out that he did not keep in mind consistently the distinction between these two theories of procedure.

The Method of Analysis and Synthesis and the Axiomatic Method share as a common objective the explanation and prediction of phenomena. But they differ in an important respect, particularly if one takes a narrow view of what techniques qualify as "induction". The natural philosopher who follows the Method of Analysis seeks to generalize from the results of observation and experiment. The Axiomatic Method, by contrast, places greater emphasis on the creative imagination. The natural philosopher who adopts this method may begin anywhere. But the axiom system he creates is relevant to science only if it can be linked to what can be observed.

"HYPOTHESES NON FINGO"

Newton agreed with Galileo that primary qualities are the proper subject matter of physics. According to Newton, the starting-point and end-point of scientific inquiry is the determination of the values of "manifest qualities", those aspects of phenomena that may be measured experimentally.

Newton sought to restrict the content of his "experimental philosophy" to statements about manifest qualities, "theories" derived from these statements, and queries directive of further inquiry. In particular, he sought to exclude "hypotheses" from experimental philosophy.

Newton's use of the terms 'theory' and 'hypothesis' does not conform to modern usage. He applied the term 'theory' to invariant relations among terms designating manifest qualities. He sometimes spoke of these invariant relations as relations "deduced from" phenomena, but he most likely meant by this that there was very strong inductive evidence for certain of these relations. 'Hypotheses', in one of Newton's usages*, are statements about terms that designate "occult qualities" for which no measuring procedures are known.

Newton was quick to take offence whenever his experimentally based "theories" were labelled "hypotheses". For example, when the mathematician Pardies incautiously referred to Newton's theory of colours as a "very ingenious hypothesis",[16] Newton promptly corrected him. Newton emphasized that there was conclusive experimental evidence that sunlight comprises rays of differing colours and refractive properties. He distinguished carefully his "theory" that light has certain properties of refraction, from any "hypothesis" about waves or corpuscles by which these properties might be explained.[17]

Newton defended a similar position on the "theory" of gravitational attraction. He insisted that he had established the existence of gravitational attraction and its mode of operation, thereby accounting for the motions of the planets, the tides, and diverse other phenomena. But he did not wish to jeopardize this "theory" by tying it to a particular hypothesis about the underlying cause of the attraction. "I feign no hypotheses", he wrote.[18]

His injunction was directed primarily against "explanations" of gravitational attraction in terms of the Cartesian hypothesis of invisible swirling vortices of ether. Newton demonstrated in the *Principia* that Descartes's Vortex Hypothesis had consequences that are not in agreement with the observed motions of the planets.

* I. B. Cohen has discussed nine meanings of 'hypothesis' in Newton's writings (*Franklin and Newton*, 138–40).

Yet in other contexts, Newton was willing to entertain hypotheses that explain correlations among manifest qualities. Indeed, he himself flirted with a hypothesis about an ethereal medium which produces gravitational attraction. However, Newton emphasized that the function of such hypotheses is to direct future research, and not to serve as premises for sterile disputation.

THE RULES OF REASONING IN PHILOSOPHY

To direct the search for *fruitful* explanatory hypotheses, Newton suggested four regulative principles, referred to as "hypotheses" in the first edition of the *Principia*, and "rules of reasoning in philosophy" in the second edition. These regulative principles are:

I.   We are to admit no more causes of natural things than such as are both true and sufficient to explain their appearances.

II. Therefore to the same natural effects we must, as far as possible, assign the same causes.

III. The qualities of bodies, which admit neither intensification nor remission of degrees, and which are found to belong to all bodies within the reach of our experiments, are to be esteemed the universal qualities of all bodies whatsoever.

IV. In experimental philosophy we are to look upon propositions inferred by general induction from phenomena as accurately or very nearly true, notwithstanding any contrary hypotheses that may be imagined, till such time as other phenomena occur, by which they may either be made more accurate, or liable to exceptions.[19]

In support of Rule I, Newton appealed to a principle of parsimony, declaring that nature "affects not the pomp of superfluous causes". But exactly what Newton meant, or should have meant, by a "true cause" has been a subject of some debate. For instance, both William Whewell and John Stuart Mill criticised Newton for failing to specify criteria for the identification of true causes. Whewell remarked that if Newton meant to restrict the "true cause" of a type of phenomena to causes already known to be effective in producing other types of phenomena, then Rule I would be overly restrictive. It would preclude the introduction of new causes. However, Whewell was not certain that this was Newton's intended meaning. He noted that Newton may have meant only to restrict the introduction of causes to those "similar in kind" to causes that previously have been established. Whewell observed that, thus interpreted,

Rule I would be too vague to guide scientific inquiry. Any hypothetical cause could be claimed to display *some* similarity to previously established causes. Having dismissed these inadequate alternatives, Whewell suggested that what Newton should have meant by a "true cause" is a cause represented in a theory, which theory is supported by inductive evidence acquired from analysis of diverse types of phenomena.*

Mill likewise interpreted "true cause" so as to reflect his own philosophical position. Consistent with his view of induction as a theory of proof of causal connection, Mill maintained that what distinguishes a "true cause" is that its connection with the effect ascribed to it be susceptible to proof by independent evidence.†

Commenting on Rule III, Newton indicated that the qualities which satisfy the rule include extension, hardness, impenetrability, mobility, and inertia. Newton maintained that these qualities should be taken to be the universal qualities of all bodies whatsoever. Moreover, he insisted that these also are the qualities of the minute parts of bodies. In Query 31 of the *Opticks*, he set forth a research programme to uncover the forces that govern the interactions of the minute parts of bodies. Newton expressed the hope that the study of short-range forces would achieve an integration of physico-chemical phenomena such as changes of state, solution, and the formation of compounds, in much the same way as the principle of universal gravitation had achieved the integration of terrestrial and celestial dynamics. Subsequently, Newton's research programme received theoretical development from Boscovich and Mossotti, and practical implementation in the electromagnetic researches of Faraday and the various attempts to measure the elective affinities of the chemical elements.‡

THE CONTINGENT NATURE OF SCIENTIFIC LAWS

Newton repudiated the Cartesian programme of deducing scientific laws from indubitable metaphyical principles. And he denied that a necessary knowledge of scientific laws can be achieved in any manner. According to Newton, the natural philosopher may establish

---

* Whewell's concept of a "consilience of inductions" is discussed in Chapter 9.
† Mill's view of causal relation is discussed in Chapter 9.
‡ The role of Newton's research programme in eighteenth-century science has been discussed by A. Thackray in *Atoms and Powers* (Cambridge, Mass.: Harvard University Press, 1970).

that phenomena are related in a certain way, but cannot establish that the relation could not be otherwise.

It is true that Newton did suggest that if we could know the forces that operate on the minute particles of matter, we could understand why macroscopic processes occur in the ways they do. But Newton did not maintain that such knowledge would constitute a necessary knowledge of nature. On the contrary, he held that all interpretations of natural processes are contingent and subject to revision in the light of further evidence.

REFERENCES

[1] Isaac Newton, *Opticks* (New York: Dover Publications, 1952), 404.

[2] Ibid., 45–8.

[3] Newton, *Mathematical Principles of Natural Philosophy*, trans. by A. Motte, revised by F. Cajori (Berkeley: University of California Press, 1962), II, 547.

[4] Ibid., I, 8.

[5] Ibid., I, 7–8.

[6] Newton, *Unpublished Scientific Papers of Isaac Newton*, trans. and ed. by A. R. Hall and M. B. Hall (Cambridge: Cambridge University Press, 1962), 132–43.

[7] Newton, *Mathematical Principles*, I, 10–11.

[8] Ernst Mach, *The Science of Mechanics*, trans. by T. J. McCormack (La Salle: Open Court Publishing Co., 1960), 271–97.

[9] Newton, *Mathematical Principles*, I. 8.

[10] Ibid., I, 13.

[11] Newton, *Opticks*, 154–8.

[12] I. Bernard Cohen, *Franklin and Newton* (Philadelphia, Pa.: The American Philosophical Society, 1956), 139.

[13] Newton, *Mathematical Principles*, I, 10.

[14] Newton, *Unpublished Scientific Papers*, 127.

[15] For example, see S. Toulmin, 'Newton on Absolute Space, Time, and Motion', *Phil. Rev.* 68 (1959); E. Nagel, *The Structure of Science* (New York: Harcourt, Brace and World, 1961), 179–83.

[16] Ignatius Pardies, 'Some Animadversions on the Theory of Light of Mr. Isaac Newton', in *Isaac Newton's Papers and Letters on Natural Philosophy*, ed. by I. B. Cohen (Cambridge, Mass.: Harvard University Press, 1958), 86.

[17] Newton, 'Answer to Pardies', in *Isaac Newton's Papers and Letters on Natural Philosophy*, 106.

[18] Newton, *Mathematical Principles*, II, 547. See also A. Koyré, *Newtonian Studies* (Cambridge, Mass.: Harvard University Press, 1965), 35–6.

[19] Newton, *Mathematical Principles*, II, 398–400.

9

Analyses of the Implications of the New Science for a Theory of Scientific Method

---

I. The Cognitive Status of Scientific Laws

JOHN LOCKE (1632–1704) was born at Wrington (Somerset). He was educated at Oxford and was appointed lecturer in Greek and philosophy there in 1660. Subsequently, he became interested in medicine and obtained a licence to practise, again from Oxford.

In 1666, Locke joined the service of the first Earl of Shaftesbury, and became physician, friend, and adviser to this influential politician. Upon Shaftesbury's fall from power, Locke chose exile in Holland. It was during his stay in Holland that Locke completed his *Essay Concerning Human Understanding* (1690), in which he set forth his views on the prospects and limitations of science. Locke's political fortunes improved upon the accession of William of Orange in 1689. He returned to England and accepted a position in the Civil Service.

GOTTFRIED WILHELM LEIBNIZ (1646–1716) was the son of the Professor of Moral Philosophy at the University of Leipzig. An omnivorous reader, Leibniz studied philosophy at his father's university, and jurisprudence at Jena.

Leibniz spent much of his adult life at court, first at Mainz and later at Hanover. During this service he was entrusted with diplomatic missions which enabled him to establish contact with numerous political and intellectual leaders. Leibniz worked tirelessly for legal reform, for Protestant religious unification, and for the advancement of science and technology. He maintained extensive correspondences with the leading thinkers of his day and actively promoted scientific co-operation by means of his membership in the Royal Society, the French Academy, and the Prussian Academy. It is ironic that his later years were marked by bitter polemics with the followers of Newton over priorities in the invention of the calculus.

DAVID HUME (1711–76) enrolled to study law at the University of Edinburgh, but left without receiving a degree. He neglected his legal studies for the pursuit of philosophy. Hume spent several years at Rheims and La Flèche, where he completed work on the *Treatise of Human Nature* (1739–40).

Hume was greatly disappointed with the reception accorded this book which "fell deadborn from the press". Undaunted, he revised and popularized the *Treatise* in *An Enquiry Concerning Human Understanding* (1748). Hume also published an *Enquiry Concerning the Principles of Morals* (1751), and a lengthy *History of England* (1754–62).

Hume was rebuffed in his attempts to secure positions at the Universities of Edinburgh and Glasgow. His opponents alleged heresy and even atheism. In 1763 Hume was appointed secretary to the British ambassador to France, and subsequently was lionized by Parisian society.

IMMANUEL KANT (1724–1804) spent his entire life in the immediate vicinity of his native Königsberg. He studied philosophy and theology at the University of Königsberg, and became Professor of Logic and Metaphysics there in 1770. Kant's views on the importance of regulative principles in scientific inquiry are set forth in *Critique of Pure Reason* (1781), and *Critique of Judgment* (1790).

LOCKE ON THE POSSIBILITY OF A NECESSARY KNOWLEDGE OF NATURE

JOHN LOCKE, who like Newton was committed to atomism, specified the conditions that would have to be fulfilled to achieve a necessary knowledge of nature. According to Locke, we would have to know both the configurations and motions of atoms and the ways in which the motions of atoms produce ideas of primary and secondary qualities in the observer. He noted that if these two conditions could be fulfilled, then we would know *a priori* that gold must dissolve in *aqua regis* but not *aqua fortis*, that rhubarb must have a purgative effect, and that opium must make a man sleepy.[1]

Locke held that we are ignorant of the configurations and motions of atoms. But his usual position was that this ignorance is a contingent matter, a question of the extreme minuteness of atoms. In principle, we might be able to overcome this ignorance. But even if this were achieved, we still could not reach a necessary knowledge of phenomena. This is because we are ignorant of the ways in which atoms manifest certain powers. Locke held that the atomic constituents of a body possess the power, in virtue of their motions, to produce in us ideas of secondary qualities such as colours and sounds. Moreover, the atoms of a particular body have the power to affect the atoms of other bodies so as to alter the ways in which these bodies affect our senses.[2] At one point, Locke declared that only by divine revelation could we know the ways in which atomic motions produce these effects in us.[3]

In some passages, Locke held that an unbridgeable epistemological gap separates the "real world" of atoms and the realm of ideas that constitutes our experience. And he expressed no interest in entertaining hypotheses about atomic structure. It is a curious feature of Locke's philosophy of science that although he consistently attributed macroscopic effects to atomic interactions, he made no attempt to correlate specific effects with particular hypotheses about atomic motions. As Yolton has pointed out, Locke instead recommended for science a Baconian methodology of correlation and exclusion, based on the compilation of extensive natural histories.[4] This involved a shift in focus from "real essences"—the atomic configurations of bodies—to "nominal essences"—the observed properties and relations of bodies.

Locke insisted that the most that can be achieved in science is a collection of generalizations about the association and succession of "phenomena". These generalizations are probable at best, and do not satisfy the rationalist ideal of necessary truth. In this vein, Locke sometimes downgraded natural science. In one passage, he conceded that the trained scientist views nature in a more sophisticated way than does an untrained observer, but he insisted that this is "but judgment and opinion, not knowledge and certainty".[5]

Yet in other passages, Locke drew back from the sceptical possibilities implicit in his distinction between the primary properties of the atomic constituents of bodies, which properties exist independently of our perceptual experiences, and our ideas of secondary qualities. He believed that there do exist necessary connections in nature, even though these connections are opaque to human understanding. Locke often used the term 'idea' in such a way as to bridge the epistemological gap. In this usage, "ideas" are effects of operations in the "real world" of atoms. The idea of a red patch, for example, is a possession of a perceiving subject, but it also is an effect somehow produced by processes external to the subject (in normal viewing situations at least). Locke was confident that it is the motions of the atomic constituents of matter that give rise to our ideas of colours and tastes, even though we cannot learn just how this takes place. It remained for Berkeley and Hume to demand that the warrant be produced for this assumption.

LEIBNIZ ON THE RELATIONSHIP BETWEEN SCIENCE AND METAPHYSICS

Locke's contemporary Leibniz gave a more optimistic assessment of what can be achieved in science. Leibniz was a practising scientist who made important contributions to mathematics and physics. And he confidently extrapolated from his scientific findings to metaphysical assertions. Indeed, Leibniz set up a two-way commerce between scientific theories and metaphysical principles. Not only did he support his metaphysical principles by analogical arguments based on scientific theories. He also employed metaphysical principles to direct the search for scientific laws.

A case in point is the relationship between studies of impact phenomena and the principle of continuity. Leibniz used the principle of continuity to criticize Descartes's rules of impact. He noted that, according to Descartes, if two bodies of equal size and speed collide head-on, their speeds after impact are the same, but in reversed directions; but that if one body is larger than the other, both bodies proceed after impact in the direction in which the larger body was travelling. Leibniz objected that it is unreasonable that an infinitesimal addition of matter would result in a discontinuous change of behaviour.[6] And having corrected Descartes's rules of impact, Leibniz was quite willing to appeal to impact phenomena to support the ontological claim that nature invariably acts so as to avoid discontinuities.

A similar reciprocal interaction is present in Leibniz's discussion of the relationship between *extremum* principles in physics and the principle of perfection. For instance, he argued that because nature always selects the easiest, or most direct, course of action from among a set of alternatives, the passage of a light ray from one medium into another obeys Snel's Law.* Leibniz derived Snel's Law by applying the differential calculus which he had developed to the condition that the "path difficulty" of the ray (the path length times the resistance of the medium) is a minimum. And he took his success in this enterprise as support for the metaphysical principle that God governs the universe in such a way that a maximum of "simplicity" and "perfection" be realized.[7]

Further evidence of Leibniz's view of the interdependence of physics and metaphysics is the relationship between the conservation of *vis viva* (mv^2) and the principle of monadic activity. On the one hand, Leibniz argued analogically from the conservation of *vis viva* in physical processes to a characterization of being-as-such as an "internal striving". On the other hand, his conviction that monadic activity on the metaphysical plane must have its correlate on the physical plane directed his attention to a search for some "entity" that is conserved in physical interactions.

Buchdahl has called attention to the importance of Leibniz's metaphysical commitment by contrasting the analyses of collision processes given by Huygens and Leibniz. Whereas Huygens merely noted in passing that mv^2, regarded as the product of mathematical parameters, remained constant in such processes, Leibniz "substantialized" *vis viva* and held that its conservation was a general physical principle.[8]

Leibniz sought to interpret the universe in such a way that the mechanistic world-view, which focuses on material and efficient causation, is supported by teleological considerations. *Extremum*

*See p. 159n.

principles, conservation principles, and the principle of continuity were well suited to effect the desired integration of the mechanistic and teleological standpoints. In the case of *extremum* principles, for example, the teleological connotation is that natural processes occur in certain ways *in order that* certain quantities achieve a minimum (or maximum) value. It is a short step, and one that Leibniz was anxious to take, to the position that a Perfect Being created the universe in such a way that natural processes satisfy these principles.

Locke had bemoaned the fact that we cannot advance from a knowledge of the association of qualities to a knowledge of the internal constitutions or "real essences" of things. Leibniz took quite a different attitude towards this epistemological gap. He conceded that, at the level of phenomena, scientists can reach only probability, or "moral certainty". But he was convinced that the general metaphysical principles he had formulated were necessary truths. Of necessity, individual substances (monads) unfold in accordance with a principle of perfection that ensures their harmonious interrelation. And we can be certain that this monadic activity "underlies" phenomena. But we cannot know that the metaphysical principles *must* be instantiated, at the level of phenomena, in one particular way.

As a rule, Leibniz emphasized the certainty of his metaphysical principles rather than the contingent nature of empirical knowledge. His dominant posture was one of optimism. Indeed, at times he appeared to claim more than probability for empirical generalizations. This inconsistency perhaps may be attributed to an overriding concern to establish the dependence of the phenomenal realm on the metaphysical realm.

Leibniz recognized that a picture of a metaphysical realm "behind" phenomena is of interest only if there are strong links between the two realms. The strongest possible links would be deductive relationships between metaphysical principles and empirical laws. Given the necessary status of metaphysical principles, deductive relationships would extend the domain of necessary connectedness into the realm of phenomena.

Leibniz flirted with this possibility. He employed an analogy based on the theory of infinite series to suggest that there are strong links between the two realms. The analogy is that metaphysical principles are related to physical laws much as the law that generates an infinite series is related to the particular members of that series.[9]

But even if one were to accept the force of this analogy, this would not establish that metaphysical principles *imply* empirical laws. One cannot deduce, from the law of a series alone,

$$\left(\text{e.g.} \sum_{n=1}^{\infty} \frac{1}{n^2} \right),^*$$

the value of a particular member of the series. The position of the term in the series must be specified (e.g. $n = 5$). Similarly, one cannot deduce from metaphysical principles alone specific empirical laws. The way in which a metaphysical principle is realized in experience must be specified. But on Leibniz's own admission, we cannot know that a metaphysical principle *must* be realized in one specific way.

I think Leibniz was aware that the infinite-series analogy could not be pressed. On other occasions he spoke of physical forces as the "echoes" of metaphysical forces,[10] a characterization that is extremely vague. And to retreat to this position was to leave unresolved the general problem of the relationship between the two realms, as well as the particular problem about the cognitive status of *extremum* principles and conservation principles *as applied in science*.

HUME'S SCEPTICISM

David Hume extended and made consistent Locke's sceptical approach to the possibility of a necessary knowledge of nature. Hume consistently denied that a knowledge of atomic configurations and interactions—even if it could be achieved—would constitute a necessary knowledge of nature. According to Hume, even if our faculties were "fitted to penetrate into the internal fabric" of bodies, we could gain no knowledge of a necessary connectedness among phenomena. The most we could hope to learn is that certain configurations and motions of atoms have been constantly conjoined with certain macroscopic effects. But knowing that a constant conjunction has been observed is not the same thing as knowing that a particular motion *must* produce a particular effect. Hume held that Locke was wrong to suggest that if we knew the atomic configuration

$$^* \sum_{n=1}^{\infty} \frac{1}{n^2} = 1 + \frac{1}{4} + \frac{1}{9} + \frac{1}{16} + \ldots = \frac{\pi^2}{6}.$$

of gold then we would understand without trial that this substance must be soluble in *aqua regia*.

Hume's denial of the possibility of a necessary knowledge of nature was based on three explicitly stated premisses: (1) all knowledge may be subdivided into the mutually exclusive categories "relations of ideas" and "matters of fact"; (2) all knowledge of matters of fact is given in, and arises from, sense impressions; and (3) a necessary knowledge of nature would presuppose knowledge of the necessary connectedness of events. Hume's arguments in support of these premisses were widely influential in the subsequent history of the philosophy of science.

Subdivision of Knowledge

Hume maintained that statements about relations of ideas and statements about matters of fact differ in two respects. The first respect is the type of truth-claim that can be made for the two types of statements. Certain statements about relations of ideas are necessary truths. For instance, given the axioms of Euclidean geometry, it could not be otherwise than that the sum of angles of a triangle is 180 degrees.* To affirm the axioms and deny the theorem is to construct a self-contradiction. Statements about matters of fact, on the other hand, are never more than contingently true. The denial of an empirical statement is not a self-contradiction; the state of affairs described could have been otherwise.

The second point of difference is the method followed to ascertain the truth or falsity of the respective types of statements. The truth or falsity of statements about relations of ideas is established independently of any appeal to empirical evidence. Hume subdivided statements about relations of ideas into those which are intuitively certain and those which are demonstratively certain. For example, the axioms of Euclidean geometry are intuitively certain; their truth is established upon examination of the meanings of their component terms. The Euclidean theorems are demonstratively certain; their truth is established by demonstrating that they are deductive consequences of the axioms. Any appeal to the measurement of figures drawn on paper or in sand is wholly irrelevant. Hume

---

* Hume denied that the propositions of geometry were necessary truths in *A Treatise of Human Nature* (1739), but subsequently changed his mind. In the *Enquiry Concerning Human Understanding* (1748), he held that geometrical propositions, as well as the propositions of arithmetic and algebra, are necessary truths.

declared that "though there never were a circle or triangle in nature, the truths demonstrated by Euclid would for ever retain their certainty and evidence."[11]

The truth or falsity of statements about matters of fact, on the other hand, must be established by an appeal to empirical evidence. One cannot establish the truth of a statement that something has happened, or will happen, simply by thinking about the meaning of words.

Hume thus effected a demarcation of the necessary statements of mathematics from the contingent statements of empirical science, thereby sharpening Newton's distinction between a formal deductive system and its application to experience. Albert Einstein later rephrased Hume's insight as follows: "as far as the laws of mathematics refer to reality, they are not certain; and as far as they are certain, they do not refer to reality."[12] Hume's demarcation placed a roadblock in the path of any naïve Pythagoreanism which seeks to read into nature a necessary mathematical structure.

The Principle of Empiricism

Hume maintained that Descartes was wrong to hold that we possess innate ideas of mind, God, body, and world. According to Hume sense impressions are the sole source of knowledge of matters of fact.* He thus echoed Aristotle's dictum that there is nothing in the intellect which was not first in the senses. Hume's version was that "all our ideas are nothing but copies of our impressions, or, in other words, that it is impossible for us to think of any thing, which we have not antecedently felt, either by our external or internal senses."[13]

Hume's thesis is both a psychological hypothesis about the genesis of empiricial knowledge and a logical stipulation of the range of empirically significant concepts. Hume restricted empirically significant concepts to those which can be "derived from" impressions.[14] Thus stated, Hume's criterion is quite vague. Elsewhere in the *Enquiry*, he suggested that the role of the mind in generating knowledge is restricted to the compounding, transposing, augmenting, or diminishing, of the ideas "copied from" impressions.[15] Presumably, any concept is excluded which is neither a "copy" of an impression nor the result of a process of compounding, transposing, augmenting, or diminishing. Concepts excluded by Hume himself include "a

* Hume included among "sense impressions" desires, volitions, and feelings, as well as visual, auditory, tactile, and olfactory data.

vacuum",[16] "substance",[17] "perduring selfhood",[18] and "necessary connectedness of events".[19]

Hume's analysis has been interpreted as reinforcing Baconian inductivism, a tradition that perhaps owes as much to Hume's epistemological investigations as to the counsel of Francis Bacon himself. Thus interpreted, Hume has been held to claim that science begins with sense impressions and can encompass only those concepts which are "constructed" somehow out of sense data. Such a view is consistent with the Method of Analysis, but not with Newton's axiomatic method.

But although this reading of Hume has been influential it fails to do justice to the complexity of Hume's position. For Hume acknowledged that the formulation of comprehensive theories, such as Newton's mechanics, is achieved by a creative insight not reducible to a "compounding, transposing, augmenting, or diminishing" of ideas "copied from" impressions. What he did deny, however, is that any such theories could achieve the status of necessary truth.

Analysis of Causation

Bacon and Locke had discussed the question of a necessary knowledge of nature from a scholastic standpoint. Both had focused on natural kinds, or species, and had sought a necessary knowledge of the coexistence of properties. Hume shifted the search for necessary empirical knowledge to sequences of events. He asked whether a necessary knowledge of such sequences was possible, and decided that it was not. Hume held that to establish a necessary knowledge of a sequence of events one would have to prove that the sequence could not have been otherwise. But Hume pointed out that it was not a self-contradiction to affirm that although every A has been followed by a B, the next A will not be followed by a B.

Hume undertook to examine our idea of a "causal relation". He noted that if we mean by a 'causal relation' both 'constant conjunction' and 'necessary connection', then we can achieve no causal knowledge at all. This is because we have no impression of any force or power by means of which an A is constrained to produce a B. The most that we can establish is that events of one type invariably have been followed by events of a second type. Hume concluded that the only "causal" knowledge that we can hope to achieve is a knowledge of the *de facto* association of two classes of events.

Hume conceded that we do feel that there is something necessary about many sequences. According to Hume, this feeling is an impression of the "internal sense", an impression derived from custom. He declared that "after a repetition of similar instances, the mind is carried by habit, upon the appearance of one event, to expect its usual attendant, and to believe that it will exist."[20] Of course, the fact that the mind comes to anticipate a *B* upon the appearance of an *A* is no proof that there is a necessary connection between *A* and *B*.

Consistent with this analysis, Hume stipulated definitions of 'causal relation' both from an objective and from a subjective standpoint. Objectively considered, a causal relation is a constant conjunction of the members of two classes of events; subjectively considered, a causal relation is a sequence such that, upon appearance of an event of the first class, the mind is led to anticipate an event of the second class.

These two definitions appear both in the *Treatise* and in the *Enquiry*.[21] However, in the *Enquiry*, Hume inserted after the first definition the following qualification: "or in other words where, if the first object had not been, the second never had existed."[22] Replacing the term 'object' by 'event', which is consistent with Hume's own usage, it is evident that this new definition is not equivalent to the first definition. For instance, in the case of two similar pendulum clocks arranged to be 90° out-of-phase, the ticks of the two clocks are constantly conjoined, but this does not imply that if the pendulum of clock 1 were arrested, then clock 2 would cease to tick.

Hume's inclusion of this qualification in the *Enquiry* may indicate that he was not quite satisfied to equate causal relation and *de facto* regularity. Another likely indication of his uneasiness is the fact that he included in the *Treatise*, tersely and without comment, a list of eight "Rules by which to judge of Causes and Effects".[23] Among these rules are versions of the Methods of Agreement, Difference, and Concomitant Variations, later made famous by Mill.

The Method of Difference, in particular, enables the investigator to judge causal connection upon observation of just two instances. It would seem, in this case, that Hume contradicted his "official position" that we term a relation "causal" only upon experience of a constant conjunction of two types of events. Hume denied this. He maintained that although belief that a succession of events is a causal sequence may arise even after a single observation of the sequence, the belief nevertheless is a product of custom. This is because the judgement of causal connection in such cases depends implicitly on the generalization that like objects in like circumstances produce like effects. But this generalization itself expresses our expectation based on extensive experience of constantly conjoined events. Hence our belief in a causal connection invariably is a matter of habitual expectation.

Having thus accounted for the *origin* of our belief in causal connection, Hume was quick to point out that no appeal to the regularity of past experience can guarantee fulfilment of our expectations about the future. He stated that "it is impossible, therefore, that any arguments from experience can prove this resemblance of the past to the future; since all these arguments are founded on the supposition of that resemblance."[24] Hence it is not possible to achieve a demonstrative knowledge of causes from premisses which state matters of fact.

Hume thus completed a sweeping attack on the possibility of a necessary knowledge of nature. Such knowledge would have to be either immediate or demonstrative. Hume had shown that no immediate knowledge of causes is possible, for we have no impression of necessary connection. He also had shown that it is not possible to achieve a demonstrative knowledge of causes, either from premisses which state *a priori* true relations of ideas, or from premisses which state matters of fact. There seemed to be no further possibility. No scientific interpretation can achieve the certainty of a statement such as 'the whole is greater than each of its parts.' Probability is the only defensible claim that can be made for scientific laws and theories.

Although Hume's scepticism was apprehended as a threat to science by those who were not satisfied with "merely probable" knowledge, Hume himself was quite ready to rely on the testimony of past experience. On the practical level, Hume was not a sceptic. He declared that

custom, then, is the great guide of human life. It is that principle alone which renders our experience useful to us. . . . Without the influence of custom, we should be entirely ignorant of every matter of fact beyond what is immediately present to the memory and senses.[25]

KANT ON REGULATIVE PRINCIPLES IN SCIENCE

Response to Hume

Immanuel Kant professed to be greatly disturbed by Hume's analysis of causation. Kant conceded that if the form and content of scientific laws wholly derive from sense experience, as Hume had urged, then there is no escape from Hume's conclusion. However, Kant was unwilling to grant Hume's premiss. Against Hume, he argued that although all empirical knowledge "arises from" sense impressions, it is not the case that all such knowledge is "given in" these impressions. Kant distinguished between the matter and the form of cognitive experience. He held that sense impressions provide the raw material of empirical knowledge, but that the knowing subject itself is responsible for the structural-relational organization of this raw material.

Kant believed that Hume had oversimplified the knowing process by reducing the operations of the mind to a mere "compounding, transposing, augmenting, and diminishing" of ideas "copied from" impressions. Kant's own theory of knowledge was more complex. He specified three stages in the cognitive organization of experience. First, unstructured "sensations" are ordered with respect to Space and Time (the "Forms of the Sensibility"). Second, the "perceptions" thus ordered are related by means of such concepts as Unity, Substantiality, Causality, and Contingency (four of the twelve "Categories of the Understanding"). Third, the "judgements of experience" thus formed are organized into a single system of knowledge through application of "Regulative Principles of Reason".

Kant's View of Cognitive Experience

According to Kant, Hume's inadequate theory of knowledge was associated with an equally inadequate theory of science. Kant believed that Hume was preoccupied with inductive generalization. Kant held that this emphasis draws attention from the most important feature of science—the attempt to achieve a systematic organization of knowledge. Kant was profoundly impressed by the scope and power of Euclidean geometry and Newtonian mechanics and he attributed this scope and power to the deductive structure of these disciplines.

Kant regarded the systematic organization of experience as a goal to be sought by the knowing subject. He believed that progress towards the desired systematization is achieved through the application of regulative principles. In Kant's theory of knowledge, the faculty of Reason prescribes to the Understanding certain rules for the ordering of empirical judgements. Kant was quite clear that the regulative principles of Reason cannot be used to justify any particular system of empirical judgements. Rather, they prescribe ways in which scientific theories may be constructed so as to conform to the ideal of systematic organization.

Kant formulated criteria of acceptability which reflect this emphasis on the systematic organization of experience. With respect to individual empirical laws, Kant downplayed instance-confirmation, in which deductive consequences of laws are seen to be in agreement with observations. He believed the incorporation of laws into deductive systems to be more important. Kant would hold, for instance, that although Kepler's laws do gain support from data on planetary motions, they gain further, and more important, support from their "incorporation" into Newton's theory of mechanics.

With respect to theories, Kant cited as criteria of acceptability predictive power and testability. He noted that successful theories bind together empirical laws by means of reference to new entities or relations. Implicit in this systematization is the possibility of extending the interpretation of these entities or relations to further regions of experience. Kant drew attention to the fertility of scientific theories. He suggested that those theories are most acceptable which extend our knowledge of relations among phenomena.

The Analogies of Experience and the Science of Mechanics

In the *Critique of Pure Reason*, Kant singled out three "analogies of experience" which are associated with the Categories of Substance,

Causality, and Interaction. He maintained that these analogies stipulate necessary conditions of the very possibility of objective empirical knowledge. The first analogy—the principle of the permanence of substance—specifies that substance is conserved throughout all changes. The second analogy—the principle of causality—specifies that for every event, there is some set of antecedent circumstances from which the event follows according to a rule. And the third analogy—the principle of community—specifies that substances perceived as coexistent in space are in interaction with one another.

In the *Metaphysical Foundations of Natural Science*, Kant sought to explain how these analogies apply to the science of mechanics. According to Kant, the subject-matter of mechanics is matter in motion, in so far as this matter possesses attractive and repulsive forces. He held that, as applied to mechanics, the analogies of experience are transformed into the principles of conservation of matter, inertial motion, and equality of action and reaction, viz.:

Category	Analogy of Experience	Principle of Mechanics
Substance	Conservation of Substance	Conservation of Matter
Causality	Principle of Causality (Every event has an antecedent from which it follows in accordance with a rule)	Principle of Inertia (All changes of motion of bodies result from extrinsic forces)
Interaction	Community of Interaction (All things that exist simultaneously are reciprocally related)	Equality of Action and Reaction

Kant maintained that the three principles of mechanics are regulative principles that should guide the search for specific empirical laws. These principles stipulate that to explain an event one must find a set of prior circumstances from which events of the same type follow according to a rule, in such a way that matter is conserved, changes in the motion of a body are attributed to forces extrinsic to the body itself, and action is balanced by reaction. Kant insisted that objective empirical knowledge can be achieved only if individual laws are formulated so as to conform to these principles.

Systematic Organization of Empirical Laws

Kant held that there are further regulative principles that apply to the organization of individual laws into a systematic interpretation of nature. In the *Critique of Judgment* (1790), he declared that

the reflective judgment, which is obliged to ascend from the particular in nature to the universal, requires on that account a principle that it cannot borrow from experience, because its function is to establish the unity of all empirical principles under higher ones, and hence to establish the possibility of their systematic subordination. Such a transcendental principle, then, the reflective judgment can only give as a law from and to itself.[26]

According to Kant, the general regulative principle which the reflective judgement prescribes to itself is the Purposiveness of Nature.

Kant insisted that although we cannot prove that nature is purposively organized, we must systematize our empirical knowledge by viewing nature *as if* it were so organized. Kant believed that systematization of empirical knowledge is possible only if we act on the presupposition that an "understanding" other than our own has furnished us with particular empirical laws so arranged as to make possible for us a unified experience.

In itself, the Principle of the Purposiveness of Nature appears to tell us only that if we seek to construct a systematic subordination of empirical laws, we must act on the assumption that such an achievement is possible. Presumably we may exclude inconsistent sets of laws as incompatible with a purposive organization of nature. But this provides but a small clue as to what types of system would satisfy the Principle of Purposiveness.

Kant further specified the meaning of the Principle of Purposiveness by formulating a list of presuppositions which he believed to be suggested by that principle:

(1) that nature takes the shortest way (*lex parsimoniae*);*

(2) that nature "makes no leaps either in the course of its changes or in the juxtaposition of specifically different forms (*lex continui in natura*)";

(3) that there exist in nature only a small number of types of causal interaction;

---

* Kant was much impressed by Maupertuis's principle of least action, a principle from which—upon suitable interpretation of 'action'—laws governing static equilibrium, collisions, and refraction could be derived. The principle of least action, like Leibniz's principle of least effort, appeared to provide a reason why these individual laws are obeyed. Maupertuis interpreted the principle as evidence of the purposive activity of the Creator. Kant, however, attributed to the principle only the status of a regulative principle.

(4) that there exists in nature a subordination of species and genera comprehensible by us; and

(5) that it is possible to incorporate species under progressively higher genera.[27]

These presuppositions become regulative principles when the investigator interrogates nature on the assumption that the presuppositions are fulfilled. Kant held that these regulative principles specify how we *ought* to judge in order to achieve a systematic knowledge of nature.[28]

In the *Critique of Pure Reason*, Kant suggested three additional regulative principles to guide research in the taxonomic disciplines: a Principle of Homogeneousness, which stipulates that specific differences be disregarded so that species may be grouped into genera; a Principle of Specification, which stipulates that specific differences be emphasized so that species may be divided into subspecies; and a Principle of the Continuity of Forms, which stipulates that there be a continuous, gradual transition from species to species. Kant maintained that the Principle of Homogeneousness is a check against finding an extravagant variety of species and genera, that the Principle of Specification is a check against hasty generalization, and that the Principle of the Continuity of Forms unites the first two principles by requiring that a balance be struck between them.[29]

In addition to prescribing these various regulative principles, Kant defended the use of idealizations in scientific theories. He recognized that in many cases the systematic organization of empirical laws is facilitated by the introduction of conceptual simplification. Hence he did not wish to limit the raw material of scientific theories to concepts "derived from nature". Kant cited the concepts "pure earth", "pure water", and "pure air" as examples of idealizations not inferred from phenomena, and suggested that the use of such concepts facilitates the systematic explanation of chemical phenomena.[30] Kant's examples are less forceful than Galileo's expressly formulated idealizations "ideal pendulum" and "free fall in a vacuum", but Kant must be credited with the insight that a naïve empiricism fails to provide a sufficiently rich conceptual basis for science.

Teleological Explanations. The Principle of Purposiveness enjoins us to investigate nature *as if* the laws we discover were part of a system of laws arranged by an "understanding" other than our own. If we proceed on this basis, we are bound to inquire about the place of particular laws in the system of nature as a whole. This is particularly true in the biological sciences. We cannot help but ask questions about the purposes served by observed patterns of structure, function, and behaviour. Answers to such questions often are teleological explanations, characterized by use of the phrase 'in order that' or its equivalent.

Kant believed that teleological explanations were of value in science for two reasons. In the first place, teleological explanations are of heuristic value in the search for causal laws. Kant maintained that asking questions about "ends" may suggest new hypotheses about "means", thereby extending our knowledge of the mechanical interaction of systems and their parts.[31] In the second place, teleological interpretations contribute to the ideal of the systematic organization of empirical knowledge by supplementing the available causal interpretations. Kant believed that causal interpretations should be extended as far as possible, but he was pessimistic about the possibility of an extensive causal interpretation of life processes.

Kant's pessimism was based on his conception of the nature of living organisms. According to Kant, living organisms exhibit a reciprocal dependence of part and whole; not only is the whole what it is in virtue of an organization of parts, but also a part is what it is in virtue of its relation to the whole. Each part of a living organism is related to the whole both as cause and as effect. An organism is both an organized whole and a self-organizing whole. Kant believed that this reciprocal dependence of part and whole cannot be explained fully by causal laws. Causal laws establish only that particular states of an organism follow from other states according to a rule.

There are limitations, therefore, on a causal interpretation of nature. Kant set forth the limitations, but he did not counsel a return to an "easy teleology", in which the structures and functions of organisms are dismissed by reference to "final causes". For Kant, the proper explanation of natural phenomena is in terms of laws which state patterns according to which events occur. The concept of causality is constitutive of objective empirical knowledge; the concept of purpose is not. Kant maintained that purposiveness can be only a regulative principle by means of which Reason selects as its goal the systematic organization of empirical laws. By relocating teleology at the level of the regulative activity of Reason, Kant achieved the integration of teleological and mechanistic emphases that Leibniz had sought.

REFERENCES

[1] John Locke, *An Essay Concerning Human Understanding*, IV, iii, 25.

[2] Ibid., II, viii, 23.

[3] Ibid., IV, vi, 14.

[4] John Yolton, *Locke and the Compass of Human Understanding* (Cambridge: Cambridge University Press, 1970), 58.

[5] Locke, *Essay*, IV, xii, 10.

[6] G. W. Leibniz, 'On a General Principle Useful in Explaining the Laws of Nature through a Consideration of the Divine Wisdom; To Serve as a Reply to the Response of the Rev. Father Malebranche', in L. Loemker, ed., *Leibniz: Philosophical Papers and Letters* (Dordrecht: D. Reidel Publishing Co., 1969), 351-3.

[7] Leibniz, 'Tentamen Anagogicum: An Anagogical Essay in the Investigation of Causes', *Leibniz: Philosophical Papers and Letters*, 477-84.

[8] Gerd Buchdahl, *Metaphysics and the Philosophy of Science* (Oxford: Blackwell, 1969), 416-17.

[9] Leibniz, 'Seventh Letter to de Volder (November 10, 1703)'; 'Eighth Letter to de Volder (January 21, 1704)'; in *Leibniz: Philosophical Papers and Letters*, 533. See also George Gale, 'The Physical Theory of Leibniz', *Studia Leibnitiana II*, 2 (1970), 114-27.

[10] See Leibniz, 'Sixth Letter to de Volder (June 20, 1703)', in *Leibniz: Philosophical Papers and Letters*, 530.

[11] David Hume, *An Enquiry Concerning Human Understanding* (Chicago: The Open Court Publishing Co., 1927), 23.

[12] Albert Einstein, 'Geometry and Experience' in *Sidelights on Relativity* (New York: E. P. Dutton Co., 1923), 28.

[13] Hume, *Enquiry Concerning Human Understanding*, 63.

[14] Ibid., 19.

[15] Ibid., 16.

[16] Hume, *A Treatise of Human Nature*, 53-65.

[17] Ibid., 15-16.

[18] Ibid., 251-62.

[19] Ibid., 155-72.

[20] Hume, *Enquiry Concerning Human Understanding*, 77.

[21] Hume, *Treatise of Human Nature*, 172; *Enquiry Concerning Human Understanding*, 79.

[22] Hume, *Enquiry Concerning Human Understanding*, 79.

[23] Hume, *Treatise of Human Nature*, 173-5.

[24] Hume, *Enquiry Concerning Human Understanding*, 37.

[25] Ibid., 45.

[26] Immanuel Kant, *Kritik of Judgment*, trans. by J. H. Bernard (London: Macmillan, 1892), 17.

[27] Ibid., 20-4.

[28] Ibid., 21.
[29] Kant, *Critique of Pure Reason*, trans. by F. Max Müller (New York: Macmillan, 1934), 530.
[30] Ibid., 519.
[31] Kant, *Kritik of Judgment*, 327.

II. Theories of Scientific Procedure

JOHN HERSCHEL (1792–1871) was the son of the great astronomer William Herschel. The achievements of the elder Herschel included the discovery of Uranus and the compilation of valuable data on double stars and nebulae.

John Herschel studied at Cambridge, and thereafter devoted his life to the pursuit of science. His scientific achievements included studies of double refraction in crystals, experiments in photography and photo-chemistry, a method of computing binary-star orbits, and numerous astronomical observations. Herschel spent the period 1834–8 at the Cape of Good Hope, where he successfully extended his father's survey of double stars and nebulae to the Southern skies.

Herschel published *A Preliminary Discourse on the Study of Natural Philosophy* in 1830. His analysis of the role of hypothesis, theory, and experiment in science was acknowledged to be influential by Whewell, Mill, and Darwin, among others.

WILLIAM WHEWELL (1794–1866) graduated from Trinity College, Cambridge, where he was appointed Professor of Minerology (1828), Professor of Moral Philosophy (1838), and Vice-Chancellor (1842). He was instrumental in introducing into England the continental version of the calculus, and was largely responsible for broadening the course of study at Cambridge.

Whewell performed extensive researches on the tides, and was recognized—by Lyell and Faraday, among others—as an authority on scientific nomenclature. He completed his extensive *History of the Inductive Sciences* in 1837, and based his *Philosophy of the Inductive Sciences* (1840) on the results of this historical analysis.

ÉMILE MEYERSON (1859–1933) was born in Lublin, Russian Poland, studied at various European universities, and then combined research into the history and philosophy of science with the practice of chemistry in France. Meyerson viewed the history of science as a continuing search for that which is conserved throughout change. His published works include *Identity and Reality* (1907), and studies of quantum mechanics and the theory of relativity.

JOHN HERSCHEL'S THEORY OF SCIENTIFIC METHOD

John Herschel's *Preliminary Discourse on Natural Philosophy* (1830), was the most comprehensive and best-balanced work on the philosophy of science available at that time. Herschel was one of the foremost English scientists of his day, and his writing on scientific method was distinguished by careful analyses of recent achievements in physics, astronomy, chemistry, and geology.

One of Herschel's important contributions to the philosophy of science was a clear distinction between the "context of discovery" and the "context of justification". He insisted that the procedure used to formulate a theory is strictly irrelevant to the question of its acceptability. A meticulous inductive ascent and a wild guess are on the same footing if their deductive consequences are confirmed by observation.

Context of Discovery

Although he respected Francis Bacon's views on scientific inquiry, Herschel was aware that many important scientific discoveries do not fit the Baconian pattern. For this reason, he maintained that there are two distinct ways in which a scientist may proceed from observations to laws and theories. One approach is the application of specific inductive schema. The other is the formulation of hypotheses. Herschel's view of the context of discovery may be represented schematically as follows:

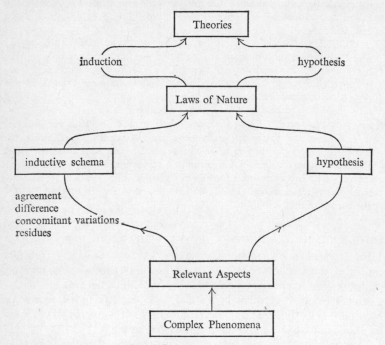

Herschel's Pattern of Discovery

According to Herschel, the first step in scientific procedure is to subdivide complex phenomena into their constituent parts or aspects, and to fix attention on those properties which are crucial for explaining the phenomena. To account for the motion of bodies, for example, one must focus on such properties as force, mass, and velocity. Herschel's principal example of the reduction of a complex phenomenon into its relevant aspects is the analysis of sound into the vibration of a source, the transmission of vibratory motion through a medium, its reception by the ear, and the production of sensation. He held that a complete understanding of sound would require a knowledge of impact phenomena which issue in vibration, a knowledge of the interaction of a moving particle and the particles which surround it, and a knowledge of the physiology of auditory sensations.[1]

Laws of Nature. Phenomena properly analysed are the raw material from which the scientist seeks to formulate "laws of nature". Herschel included among laws of nature both correlations of properties and sequences of events. Among lawful correlations of properties are Boyle's Law and the generalization that doubly refracting substances exhibit periodical colours under polarized light. Herschel spoke of such correlations as "general facts". Among lawful sequences of events are Galileo's laws of free fall and the parabolic trajectory of projectiles.

Herschel noted that laws of nature are affirmed implicitly with a stipulation that certain boundary conditions are fulfilled. For instance, the law of free fall is affirmed to hold only for motion in a vacuum, and Boyle's Law is affirmed to hold only for changes at constant temperature.

Herschel traced two distinct routes from phenomena to laws of nature. The first route to the discovery of laws is by application of specific inductive schema. Boyle's Law, for example, was discovered by studying the variation of the volume of a gas with its pressure, and generalizing from the experimental results. For example, given the data:

P	V
·5	2·0
1·0	1·0
2·0	0·5
5·0	0·2

the investigator may conclude that $P \propto (1/V)$.

The second route to the discovery of laws is by formulation of hypotheses. Herschel emphasized that this latter route to laws of nature cannot be reduced to the application of fixed rules. He cited as an example Huygens's hypothesis that the extraordinary ray in doubly-refracting Iceland spar is propagated elliptically. Even though Huygens had no conception of the transverse wave motion of light, he was able to formulate a law which accounts for double refraction by means of this hypothesis of elliptic propagation. According to Herschel, Huygens's hypothesis cannot be represented as the conclusion of an inductive schema.[2]

Theories. The discovery of laws of nature is only the first stage in scientific interpretation. The second stage is the incorporation of these laws into theories. According to Herschel, theories arise either upon further inductive generalization, or by creation of bold hypotheses that establish an interrelation of previously unconnected laws.

Herschel combined the Baconian ideal of a hierarchy of scientific generalizations with a perceptive emphasis on the role of the creative imagination in the construction of the hierarchy. One imaginative theory which impressed him was Ampère's theory of electromagnetism. Ampère explained the mutual attraction or repulsion of magnets by positing the existence of circulating electric currents within the magnets. Ampère did not arrive at this theory upon application of inductive schema to the laws of electricity and magnetism. However, the theory does have testable consequences, and Herschel insisted that its acceptability is determined, not by the method of its formulation, but by the experimental confirmation of these consequences.[3]

Context of Justification

Herschel emphasized that agreement with observations is the most important criterion of acceptability for scientific laws and theories. Moreover, he insisted that some confirming instances are of greater significance than others.

One important type of confirming instance is the extension of a law to extreme cases. Herschel noted, for example, that the identical acceleration of a coin and a feather in an experimentally produced vacuum was a "severe test" of Galileo's law of falling bodies.[4]

A second important type of confirming instance is an unexpected result which indicates that a law or theory has an undesigned scope. Herschel declared that

the surest and best characteristic of a well-founded and extensive induction ... is when verifications of it spring up, as it were, spontaneously, into notice, from quarters where they might be least expected, or even among instances of that very kind which were at first considered hostile to them.[5]

He noted, for example, that discovery of the elliptic orbits of binary star systems was unexpected confirmation of Newtonian mechanics,[6] and that the existence of a discrepancy between calculated and observed velocities of sound was an unexpected confirmation of the law of heat generation by compression of an elastic fluid.[7]

A third important type of confirming instance is the "crucial experiment". Herschel regarded crucial experiments as destruction tests which acceptable theories must survive.

He cited with admiration an experiment which had been suggested by Francis Bacon to determine whether the downward acceleration of bodies is the result of attraction of the Earth or of some mechanism internal to the bodies themselves. Bacon had suggested that the issue be decided by comparing the behaviour of a weight-driven clock and a spring-driven clock at high altitudes and in mines.[8]

In addition, Herschel credited Pascal with having designed a crucial experiment to decide whether the rise of mercury in closed tubes is the result of atmospheric pressure or of "abhorrence of a vacuum". According to Herschel, Pascal's comparison of the heights of a mercury column at the base and top of a mountain refuted the "abhorrence" hypothesis and left Torricelli's "sea of air" hypothesis alone in possession of the field.[9]

It may be objected that, whereas the proposed experiments of Bacon and Pascal may provide striking confirmation of particular hypotheses, they properly are termed "crucial" only if every possible alternative hypothesis is inconsistent with the results obtained. Failure to give due weight to this requirement led Herschel, and many other nineteenth-century scientists, to accept Foucault's determination that the velocity of light is greater in air than in water as a "crucial" experiment. Foucault's result was consistent with Huygens's wave theory, but was inconsistent with Newton's corpuscular theory. Many scientists concluded from this that light must be "really" a wave. The implicit assumption that these two theories are the only possible interpretations of optical phenomena later proved to be incorrect.

Despite the fact that too much significance has been attributed to certain experiments in the evaluation of competing theories, the general attitude which promotes a search for falsifying instances has been most important in the history of science. Herschel encouraged this attitude. He demanded that the scientist assume the role of antagonist against his own theories, and seek both direct refutations and exceptions which limit the range of application of these theories. Herschel believed that the worth of a theory is proved only by its ability to withstand such attacks.

WHEWELL'S CONCLUSIONS ABOUT THE HISTORY OF THE SCIENCES

Morphology of Scientific Progress

William Whewell, a contemporary of Herschel, sought to base his philosophy of science on a comprehensive survey of the history of science. Whewell proposed to examine the actual process of discovery in the various sciences in order to see if any patterns are displayed therein.

Whewell claimed originality for his approach, pointing out that previous writers on the philosophy of science had regarded the history of science as a mere storehouse of examples which may be cited to illustrate particular points about scientific method. Whewell proposed to invert this relationship which had made the history of science dependent on the philosophy of science.

Whewell was quite sophisticated about the methodology of historical research. He recognized that recovery of the past necessarily involves acts of synthesis on the part of the historian. Accordingly, he selected certain interpretative categories to guide his historical studies. Whewell saw scientific progress as a successful union of facts and ideas, and took the polarity of fact and idea to be the basic methodological principle for the interpretation of the history of science. Armed with this principle, he sought to show the progress of each science by tracing the discovery of its pertinent facts and the integration of these facts under appropriate ideas.

Facts and Ideas. Whewell sometimes spoke of "facts" as reports of our perceptual experience of individual objects. However, he insisted that this was just one kind of fact. Broadly considered, a fact is any piece of knowledge which is raw material for the formulation of laws and theories. From this point of view, Kepler's Laws were facts upon which Newton theorized. Whewell held that there is only a relative distinction between fact and theory. If a theory is incorporated within another theory, it becomes a fact in its own right.

Whewell termed "ideas" those rational principles which bind together facts. Ideas express the relational aspects of experience which are a necessary condition for understanding. Whewell affirmed Kant's thesis that ideas are prescribed to, and are not derived from, sensations. Whewell included among ideas both general notions such as space, time, and cause, and ideas basic to particular sciences. Examples of the latter are "elective affinity" in chemistry, "vital forces" in biology, and "natural types" in taxonomy.

Whewell conceded that there can be no such thing as a "pure fact" divorced from all ideas. Any fact about an object or process necessarily involves the ideas of space, time, or number. Consequently, even the simplest facts involve something of the nature of theory. Whewell's distinction between fact and theory is at bottom a psychological distinction. When we label something a 'fact', we usually are unaware of the way in which relational principles integrate our sense experience. For example, we take it to be a fact that a year is approximately 365 days. But this fact involves the ideas of time, number, and recurrence. We call this relation a 'fact' only because we do not attend to the associated ideas. By contrast, when we label something a 'theory', our attention is directed to the ideas applied to integrate facts. Whewell declared that 'we still have an intelligible distinction of Fact and Theory, if we consider Theory as a conscious, and Fact as an unconscious inference, from the phenomena which are presented to our senses.'[10] He believed that the concepts 'fact', 'idea', and 'theory', are of value for interpreting the history of science, even though every theory may be also a fact and every fact partakes of the nature of theory.

Pattern of Scientific Discovery. The pattern of scientific discovery which Whewell claimed to see in the history of the sciences was a three-beat progression comprising a prelude, an inductive epoch, and a sequel. The prelude consists of a collection and decomposition of facts, and a clarification of concepts. An inductive epoch arises when a particular conceptual pattern is superinduced on the facts. And its sequel is the consolidation and extension of the integration thus achieved. This pattern of discovery may be schematized as follows:

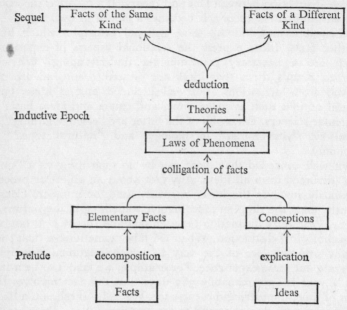

Whewell's Pattern of Discovery

Although Whewell claimed that this pattern is repeated in the history of the sciences, he was careful to point out that the stages within the pattern often overlap. Within the history of a particular science, the explication of conceptions may accompany, as well as precede, the formulation of laws, and the formulation of theories, may accompany, as well as precede, the verification of laws. Nevertheless, he claimed to have represented, by this pattern, the morphology of scientific progress.

Decomposition of Facts and Explication of Conceptions. Whewell held that the decomposition of facts and the explication of conceptions are necessary stages in theory-construction. The decomposition of facts is a reduction of complex facts to "elementary" facts which state relations among such clear and distinct ideas as space, time, number, and force. In many instances this is achieved by focusing on qualities which undergo quantitative variation, and by developing techniques for recording values of these qualities.

The notion of the explication of conceptions is more difficult to pin down. Within the history of science, discussions among scientists often result in the clarification of concepts. Whewell noted that it was through such discussions that the concepts of "force", "polarization", and "species" have been clarified, and he called for a similar clarification of the concept of "life".

One difficulty about Whewell's notion of explication is the nature of the clarification achieved. Whewell spoke of conceptions as "special modifications" of the fundamental ideas of the sciences.[11] As such, conceptions have a less extensive range of application than do the fundamental ideas themselves. Whewell included among conceptions "accelerating force" and "neutral combination of elements".[12] He held that such conceptions are explicated when their logical relations to the fundamental ideas are clearly recognized.

Whewell believed that the meaning of a fundamental idea may be expressed by a set of axioms which state basic truths about the idea. He maintained that a derivative conception is explicated only when it is related to the fundamental ideas in such a way that the "necessary cogency" of these axioms is understood. And to understand the "necessary cogency" of the axioms is "clearly and steadily" to contemplate the idea itself.[13]

The inevitable question at this point is how to recognize that a scientist has achieved a "clear and steady" apprehension of an idea. Of course, in retrospect, one can gauge the clarity of an idea by the success of the theory in which it is embedded. On this approach, one may conclude, as Whewell did, that the concept of inertia was clarified progressively in the work of Galileo, Descartes, and Newton.

Whewell maintained that, in addition to being clear, useful scientific conceptions are "appropriate" to the facts to which they are applied. He conceded that, for the most part, we can establish the appropriateness of conceptions only by pointing to confirmations of laws and theories which utilize them. Nevertheless, he thought that in certain cases the criterion of appropriateness could be used to rule out in advance misguided interpretations. For example, since the proper goal of physiology is truths respecting "vital powers", one can exclude from physiology interpretations based exclusively on mechanical principles or chemical principles.

Colligation of Facts. Whewell maintained that laws and theories are a "colligation" in which the investigator superinduces a conception upon a set of facts. He spoke of colligation as a "binding together" of facts, and chose the formulation of Kepler's Third Law to illustrate this process of integration. Kepler succeeded in binding together facts about the planets' periods of revolution and distances from the sun, by means of such conceptions as 'squares of numbers', 'cubes of distances', and 'proportionality'.[14]

According to Whewell, Kepler's achievement was a triumph of induction. He declared that in its proper use "Induction is a term applied to describe the process of a true Colligation of Facts by means of an exact and appropriate Conception".[15] Several aspects of Whewell's discussion of induction deserve comment.

Whewell held that induction is a *process* of discovery. It is not a schema for proving propositions. This is not to say that Whewell was uninterested in the problem of evaluating the evidence for inductive generalizations. But he took this to be a problem of the "logic of induction". Induction itself is the process of generalizing from facts in such a way that a colligation is achieved.

Whewell's examination of the history of science convinced him that the colligation of facts is achieved through the creative insight of scientists, and not by means of the application of specific inductive rules. He observed that the success of induction "seems to consist in framing several tentative hypotheses and selecting the right one. But a supply of appropriate hypotheses cannot be constructed by rule, nor without inventive talent."[16] According to Whewell, induction is a process of invention and trial. He cited the example of Kepler, who tried to fit the facts of planetary motion to numerous ovoid orbits, before finally achieving success with the hypothesis of elliptical orbits. In addition, Whewell listed a number of cases of "felicitous and inexplicable strokes of inventive talent" in the history of science.[17]

Whewell's principal thesis about induction is that the process of scientific discovery cannot be reduced to rules. However, he did recognize that considerations of simplicity, continuity, and symmetry often are affirmed as regulative principles in the selection of hypotheses. Whewell also suggested that specific inductive methods, such as the method of least squares and the method of residues, are of value in the formulation of mathematically quantified laws.

A corollary of Whewell's position on induction and hypothesis is that an inductive inference is always something more than a mere collection of facts. Whewell stated that "the Facts are not only brought together, but seen in a new point of view. A new mental Element is superinduced; and a peculiar constitution and discipline of mind are requisite in order to make this Induction."[18]

Tributary–River Analogy. Whewell compared the evolutionary development of a science to the confluence of tributaries to form a river.[19] He concluded from his historical studies that a science evolves through the progressive incorporation of past results in present theories. He cited Newton's theory of gravitational attraction as the paradigm of this growth by incorporation. Newton's theory subsumed Kepler's Laws, Galileo's Law of Free Fall, the motions of the tides, and diverse other facts.

Whewell was aware that successive interpretations of particular phenomena are not always consistent. Despite this, he concluded that science was a continuing progression, rather than a series of revolutions. His emphasis was on those aspects of rejected theories which facilitated subsequent theory-formation. For example, he conceded that Lavoisier's Oxygen Theory had supplanted the Phlogiston Theory, and that many facts which are explained by the Oxygen Theory are inconsistent with the Phlogiston Theory, but he contended that the Phlogiston Theory nevertheless had played a positive role in the history of chemistry, because this theory classified together the processes of combustion, acidification, and respiration.[20] On Whewell's view, a theory contributes to scientific progress if it binds together, even for the wrong reasons, facts which indeed are related.

Consilience of Inductions

Whewell claimed that the history of science reveals a clue for a "logic of induction". This clue is the tributary–river analogy. He concluded that, because scientific progress is a successive incorporation of laws into theories, an acceptable set of generalizations within a particular science ought to exhibit a certain structural pattern. This pattern is an "Inductive Table" which has the form of the tributary–river relation. The Inductive Table is an inverted pyramid, with specific facts at the top and generalizations of the broadest scope at the bottom. Transition from the top to the bottom of the table reflects progressive inductive generalization, in which observations and descriptive generalizations are subsumed under theories of increasing scope.

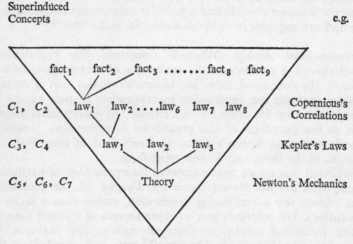

Whewell's Inductive Table

Whewell maintained that the Inductive Table specifies the form of a valid set of inductive inferences, in much the same way as the syllogism specifies the form of valid deductive inferences. However, he was careful not to over-extend the analogy. He noted that whereas the syllogistic forms are schema which are converted into valid deductive arguments upon the insertion of class names, the form of the Inductive Table is incomplete as a schema for construction of valid inductive inferences. This is because generalizations at one level are not simply conjoined to form higher generalizations. Rather, the more inclusive generalization incorporates lower-level generalizations only upon superinduction of a concept, or set of concepts. It is by means of conceptual integration, and not mere summation or enumeration, that lower-level generalizations are seen to be connected. For this reason, Whewell insisted that a *complete* Inductive Table must make reference to the specific concepts superinduced at each level of generality. For example, a table for the inductive generalization from Kepler's Laws to Newton's Laws both would display the form of an inverted pyramid, and would stipulate that the incorporation is accomplished by means of such superinduced concepts as force, inertial motion, and Absolute Space and Time.

Whewell contended that the incorporation of two or more generalizations into a more inclusive theory is itself a criterion of acceptability for scientific theories. He spoke of this incorporation as a "consilience of inductions", and declared that "No example can be pointed out, in the whole history of science, so far as I am aware, in which this Consilience of Inductions has given testimony in favour of an hypothesis afterwards discovered to be false."[21] Whether or not a consilience of inductions is achieved in a particular case depends on the adequacy of theoretical concepts to bind together two or more laws. The kinetic theory of gases is a good example of a successful consilience of inductions. The concept of Newtonian elastic collisions among molecules of a gas suffices to bind together in one theory the empirical laws of Boyle, Charles, and Graham.

Historicization of Necessary Truth

It has been indicated that Whewell interpreted the history of the sciences in terms of a Kantian distinction between the form and the content of knowledge. Scientific knowledge, for Whewell, is a binding together of facts by means of ideas. But since Whewell held that these ideas express necessary truths, it might seem that at least some scientific knowledge may achieve the status of necessary truth.

In an early work, Whewell maintained that the axioms of geometry and the fundamental laws of nature differ with regard to cognitive status. Geometrical axioms are necessary truths, the laws of the natural sciences are not.[22] Subsequently, however, he changed his mind, and insisted that some laws of the natural sciences rightly come to be recognized as necessary truths.

Whewell conceded the paradoxical nature of this claim. He agreed with Hume that no amount of empirical evidence can prove that a relationship could not be other than it is. And yet he believed that certain scientific laws have achieved necessary status.

Whewell's attempt to resolve the paradox hinged on a distinction between the *form* and the *matter* of the fundamental laws of nature.

He held that Newton's laws of motion, for instance, exemplify the *form* of the Idea of Causation. But since the Idea of Causation is a necessary condition of the very possibility of objective empirical knowledge, Newton's laws must share this necessity. According to Whewell, the meaning of the Idea of Causation may be unpacked in three axioms: (1) nothing takes place without a cause; (2) effects are proportional to their causes; and (3) reaction is equal and opposite to action. It remains for experience, however, to specify the *content* of these axioms. Experience teaches that brute matter possesses no intrinsic internal cause of acceleration, that forces are compounded in certain ways, and that certain definitions of 'action' and 'reaction' are appropriate. Newton's laws of motion express these findings. Whewell held that Newton's laws provide the proper empirical interpretation of the axioms of causation, thereby achieving the status of necessary truths.[23]

Whewell maintained that the necessary status of the fundamental laws of nature derives from their relation to those Ideas which are *a priori* necessary conditions of objective empirical knowledge. He did not specify the nature of this relation other than to appeal to the notion that such laws "exemplify" the form of the Ideas. However, he did hold that this "exemplification" takes place gradually in the historical development of the sciences. It is a matter of a progressive clarification of the relation of the most general inductive laws to the basic Ideas of the sciences. Whewell was quite certain that Newton's work established the necessary status of the general laws of mechanics. He was less certain about the other general laws of the sciences.

MEYERSON ON THE SEARCH FOR CONSERVATION LAWS

Émile Meyerson, writing in 1908, gave Whewell full credit for being the first to explain correctly the *a priori* necessity that distinguishes the fundamental laws of motion from mere empirical generalizations. Meyerson sought to extend Whewell's analysis by subdividing scientific laws into "empirical laws" and "causal laws".

According to Meyerson, an empirical law specifies how a system is altered when appropriate conditions are modified. Laws of this type enable us to predict the outcome of natural processes and to manipulate these processes to serve our ends. A causal law, by contrast, is an application of the Law of Identity to the existence of objects in time. It stipulates that there is something that remains the same throughout change. In the case of a chemical reaction, for instance, the atoms involved remain the same throughout the process of rearrangement.

Meyerson believed that whereas knowledge of empirical laws satisfies our demand for prevision, only knowledge of causal laws satisfies our desire for understanding. This is so in virtue of the dual aspect of causal laws. Because a causal law states an identity, it implies a necessary truth—"that which is, is, and cannot not be", as Aristotle said. But a causal law also has empirical content, since it states a claim about the existence of objects in time. It would seem that a causal law, according to Meyerson, implies both a necessary truth—the Law of Identity, and a contingent statement that a specific "substance" remains identical throughout changes of a given type. Meyerson conceded that the contingent statement may turn out to be false. This has happened, for example, in the case of the conservation of mass and the conservation of parity. Meyerson held that, in such cases, although the application of the Law of Identity to the existence of objects in time proves to be incorrect, the Law of Identity itself is unaffected.

But the Law of Identity itself is a tautology. It is not possible to deduce from it a single statement about the world. Meyerson recognized this. Nevertheless, he believed that the Law of Identity is a "significant" tautology. It is significant because the correct application of this law to the existence of objects in time is a necessary condition of an understanding of nature. The attempt to impress the Law of Identity upon nature is an important directive principle for scientific inquiry.[24]

The search for that which remains the same throughout change has been most successful in atomic theory and the conservation laws of mechanics. But, as Meyerson pointed out, the demand for identity which we impose upon nature is met with resistance at certain points. An example is Carnot's Principle, the Second Law of Thermodynamics. Carnot's Principle specifies that naturally occurring processes in an isolated system increase the entropy of the system. Entropy is a measure of degree of organization. An increase in entropy represents a decrease of organization within the system. But since there is a unidirectional increase of entropy in naturally occurring processes in isolated systems, it is not possible to regard entropy as a "substance" conserved throughout these processes. The Second Law of Thermodynamics is a relation of great scope and importance. It is a relation which is "non-causal" in Meyerson's sense. Meyerson declared that 'Carnot's principle is the expression of the resistance which nature opposes to the constraint which our understanding, through the principle of causality, attempts to exercise over it.'[25]

REFERENCES

[1] John F. W. Herschel, *A Preliminary Discourse on the Study of Natural Philosophy* (London: Longman etc., 1830), 88–90.

[2] J. Herschel, *Familiar Lectures on Scientific Subjects* (New York: George Routledge and Sons, 1871), 362.

[3] J. Herschel, *Preliminary Discourse*, 202–3.

[4] Ibid., 168.

[5] Ibid., 170.

[6] Ibid., 280.

[7] Ibid., 171–2.

[8] Ibid., 186–7.

[9] Ibid., 229–30.

[10] William Whewell, *Philosophy of the Inductive Sciences* (London: John W. Parker, 1847), vol. I, 42.

[11] Whewell, *Novum Organon Renovatum* (London: John W. Parker & Son, 1858), 30.

[12] Ibid., 31.

[13] Ibid., 41.

[14] Ibid., 59–60.

[15] Ibid., 70.

[16] Ibid., 59.

[17] Ibid., 64.

[18] Ibid., 71.

[19] Whewell, *History of the Inductive Sciences* (New York: D. Appleton, 1859), vol. I, 47.

[20] Ibid., II, 267–9.

[21] Whewell, *Novum Organon Renovatum*, 90.

[22] Whewell, *Astronomy and General Physics Considered with Reference to Natural Theology* (Philadelphia, Pa.: Carey, Lea and Blanchard, 1833), 164–8.

[23] Whewell, *Philosophy of the Inductive Sciences*, I, 245–54.

[24] Émile Meyerson, *Identity and Reality*, trans. by K. Loewenberg (New York: Dover Publications, 1962), 402.

[25] Ibid., 286.

III Structure of Scientific Theories

PIERRE DUHEM (1861–1916) was Professor of Physics at the University of Bordeaux (1893–1916). He made original contributions to thermo-dynamics, fluid mechanics, and the history and philosophy of science. His research on medieval physics established that the "scientific revolu-tion" of the sixteenth and seventeenth centuries had important roots in the medieval work of Buridan, Orèsme, and others. This work was a valuable corrective to that myopic view of the history of science which viewed the medieval period as a period of sterile disputation. In *The Aim and Structure of Physical Theory* (1906), Duhem maintained that scientific theories are correlative devices which group together experimental laws.

NORMAN R. CAMPBELL (1880–1949) was a Cambridge-educated physi-cist who worked for several years under J. J. Thomson at the Cavendish Laboratory, before joining the General Electric Company as a research physicist. His principal work on the philosophy of science is the posthum-ously-published *Foundations of Science* (1957), an augmented version of *Physics: The Elements* (1919). Campbell's study is distinguished by careful analyses of the theory of measurement and the structure of scientific theories.

CARL HEMPEL (1905–   ) is a German-born philosopher who studied at Göttingen, Heidelberg, and Berlin. Hempel was a member of the Berlin group that supported the aims and viewpoint of the Vienna Circle in the early 1930's. He went to the United States in 1937 and has taught at Yale and Princeton. Hempel has written important essays on the logic of scientific explanation and the structure of theories, a number of which essays are included in *Aspects of Scientific Explanation* (1965).

MARY B. HESSE (1924–) is University Reader in Philosophy of Science at Cambridge University. She studied mathematics, physics, and the history and philosophy of science at London University, and has taught at the universities of London, Leeds, and, as Visiting Professor, at Yale, Minnesota, and Chicago.

Dr. Hesse is engaged at present in developing a unified view of the structure of physical science, based on inductive inference, with particular reference to historical cases of the use of models and analogies.

R. HARRÉ (1927–) is University Lecturer in Philosophy of Science at Oxford University. He has studied mathematics and physics at the University of Auckland, and philosophy at Oxford University. Prior to his appointment at Oxford, he taught in Pakistan and at Birmingham and Leicester.

A vigorous critic of Deductivist and Positivist philosophies of science, Harré currently is engaged in a programme to redirect the methodological orientation of the social sciences.

PURE GEOMETRY AND PHYSICAL GEOMETRY

AN adequate understanding of the process of theory-construction presupposes recognition of the distinction between an axiom system and its application to experience. The construction of non-euclidean geometries in the nineteenth century called attention to this distinction. Lobachevsky, Bolyai, and Riemann invented axiom systems which differ in important respects from the euclidean system.

In the euclidean system, it is assumed that exactly one parallel line can be drawn through a point not on a given straight line. Different assumptions were made in the non-euclidean systems. Lobachevsky and Bolyai replaced the euclidean assumption by the axiom that through a given point there are two lines parallel to a given straight line. From this axiom, and the other axioms and definitions of his system, Lobachevsky deduced the theorem that the sum of the interior angles of a triangle is always less than 180°, and decreases as the areas of triangles increase. Riemann replaced the euclidean assumption by the axiom that through a point there are no lines parallel to a given straight line. A theorem of Riemann's geometry is that the sum of the interior angles of a triangle is always greater than 180°, and increases as the areas of triangles increase.

As formal deductive systems, there are no grounds for judging one of these alternatives to be superior to the others. They are consistent relative to one another. It can be shown that if euclidean geometry is internally consistent, then the alternative non-euclidean geometries are consistent as well.

Recognition of this fact led many thinkers to contrast the *a priori* status of the axioms and theorems of "pure geometry" with the empirically significant assertions of "physical geometry". Helmholtz, for instance, emphasized that the various systems of geometry are, in themselves, devoid of empirical content. It is only when they are conjoined with certain principles of mechanics that empirically significant propositions result. According to Helmholtz, it is necessary to specify how such terms as 'point', 'line', and 'angle' are to be measured before geometrical theorems can be applied to experience.[1]

DUHEM ON THE BINDING TOGETHER OF LAWS

Pierre Duhem shared Whewell's interest in the history of science and, like Whewell, sought to formulate a philosophy of science consistent with the historical record. Whewell had drawn an image of scientific progress as a confluence of tributaries to form rivers. Duhem agreed that successful theories do colligate, or bind together, experimental laws. He spoke of theories as "representing" a group of laws, and contrasted this "representative" function with an "explanatory" function that most theories are presumed to have. Theories often are held to explain phenomena by describing "the reality underlying the phenomena". Duhem criticized this view, insisting that it is the representative function alone that is of scientific value.[2]

Duhem's position that scientific theories "represent", but do not "explain", experimental laws was based on his view of the structure of theories. According to Duhem, a scientific theory consists of an axiom system and "rules of correspondence",* which correlate some of the terms of the axiom system with experimentally determined magnitudes. There may be, in addition, a picture, or model,

---

* Duhem himself did not use the phrase 'rules of correspondence' to stand for statements which link the axiom system with experimentally determined magnitudes.

associated with the interpreted axiom system. But this model is not part of the logical structure of the theory. The axiom system and rules of correspondence suffice for the deduction of those experimental laws which are "represented" by the theory. Consequently, the model associated with the theory plays no part in the task of predicting the results of experiments.

In the case of the kinetic theory of gases, for example, the axioms state relations among terms such as 'molecule', 'velocity', and 'mass'. The axiom system is linked to experience via the concept of the root-mean-square velocity of all the molecules.* Rules of correspondence correlate this root-mean-square velocity with the pressure and temperature of the gas. Duhem insisted that the kinetic theory is valuable because it binds together previously unrelated experimental laws about the macroscopic behaviour of gases. For instance, the laws attributed to Boyle, Charles, and Graham are deductive consequences of the assumptions of the theory. This is the "representative" function of the theory. He denied, however, that the model—which depicts elastic collisions between point-masses—has any explanatory function. Duhem was highly critical of Lord Kelvin's position that to "understand" a process is to visualize an underlying mechanism. According to Duhem, the model associated with a theory may have heuristic value in the search for additional experimental laws, but the model itself is not a premiss in the explanations which are given by the theory.

Duhem emphasized that a theory does not "represent" a group of laws merely by stating a conjunction of these laws. The relationship is more complex, and it allows great range to the imagination of the theorist. Of course, an acceptable theory must imply experimentally testable laws, but the fundamental assumptions of the theory may include statements about magnitudes in no way correlated with processes of measurement.[3] In such cases, the axioms of the theory are formulated by hypothesis, and not by inductive inference.

Duhem remarked that scientific procedure is impregnated throughout with theoretical considerations. He supported Whewell's

* The root-mean-square velocity u is defined as follows:

$$u = \sqrt{\left(\frac{v_1^2 + v_2^2 + v_3^2 + \ldots v_n^2}{n}\right)}$$

where n is the number of molecules.

contention that there are no irreducible facts devoid of all theory. Duhem stressed that the scientist invariably interprets experimental findings with the aid of some theory. What is of interest to the scientist is not simply that the pointer of some instrument is on 3.5. Such an observation is of value only in conjunction with an interpretation of its meaning. For instance, the pointer reading is interpreted to mean that the current in a circuit is a certain value, that the temperature of a substance has a certain value, or something similar. Moreover, as Duhem pointed out, the scientist recognizes that the instruments he employs have a finite experimental error. For example, if a manometer is read '3.5', and if its limit of experimental error is $\pm$ 0.1 atmosphere, then any pressure between 3.4 and 3.6 atmospheres is consistent with the reading. Duhem expressed this by suggesting that indefinitely many "theoretical facts" are consistent with a set of experimentally given conditions.[4]

On the basis of such considerations, Duhem criticized the ideal of scientific procedure which Newton had given in the *General Scholium* of the *Principia*. Newton had recommended that natural philosophy be restricted to propositions reached by inductive generalization from statements about phenomena. Even though Newton himself did not follow this inductivist ideal in the *Principia*, the ideal itself had proved tenacious in the history of science. Duhem observed that

two inevitable rocky reefs make the purely inductive course impracticable for the physicist. In the first place, no experimental law can serve the theorist before it has undergone an interpretation transforming it into a symbolic law; and this interpretation implies adherence to a whole set of theories. In the second place, no experimental law is exact, but only approximate, and is therefore susceptible to an infinity of distinct symbolic translations; and among all these translations, the physicist has to choose one which will provide him with a fruitful hypothesis, without his choice being guided by experiment at all.[5]

CAMPBELL ON "HYPOTHESES" AND "DICTIONARIES"

N. R. Campbell, writing in 1919, made the distinction between an axiom system and its application to experience the basis of a careful analysis of the structure of physical theories. According to Campbell, a physical theory comprises statements of two different kinds. He termed one set of statements the "hypothesis" of the theory. In Campbell's usage, a "hypothesis" is a collection of statements the truth of which cannot be ascertained empirically.[6] It makes no sense to ask about the empirical truth of a hypothesis in itself, because no empirical meaning has been assigned to its terms. Campbell included within the hypothesis of a theory both the axioms and the theorems deducible from them.

Campbell referred to the second set of statements within a theory as a "dictionary" for the hypothesis. Statements in the dictionary relate the terms of the hypothesis to statements whose empirical truth can be determined. Campbell's view of the structure of a scientific theory may be represented as follows:

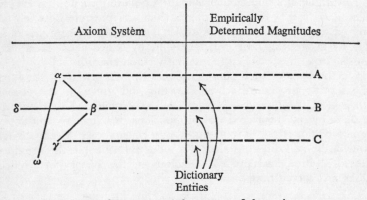

In this diagram, α, β, γ, ... are the terms of the axiom system, and the lines joining the terms represent the axioms. In itself, the axiom system is a set of abstract relations among uninterpreted terms. The boundary between the axiom system and the realm of sense experience is bridged by dictionary entries which link certain terms of the axiom system with experimentally measurable properties.

In agreement with Duhem, Campbell emphasized that in many theories there are terms for which there are no dictionary entries. It is not necessary to link every hypothetical term to experimentally testable assertions in order to achieve empirical significance for a theory as a whole. In the diagram above, δ and ω are not mentioned in the dictionary. However, the entire axiom system, within which δ and ω are terms, is linked to experience through dictionary entries relating α and A, β and B, and γ and C.

The kinetic theory of gases is a good illustration of this point. The axioms of the theory state relations among the masses and velocities of individual molecules. But there is no dictionary entry for individual molecular velocities. Nevertheless, individual molecular velocities are related to the root-mean-square velocity of all the molecules, and the root-mean-square velocity is correlated through the dictionary with the temperature and pressure of the gas.

Mathematical Theories and Mechanical Theories

Campbell subdivided physical theories into "mathematical theories" and "mechanical theories", and based the subdivision on a difference in formal structure. Each important term of the hypothesis of a mathematical theory is correlated directly and separately with empirically determined magnitudes. Physical geometry exemplifies this type of theory. Terms such as 'point', 'line', and 'angle' are linked directly to measuring procedures. In the case of a mechanical theory, on the other hand, some of the terms of the hypothesis are correlated with empirically determined magnitudes only through functions of these terms.[7] This is the case for individual molecular velocities in kinetic theory. The kinetic theory of gases thus exemplifies the mechanical type of physical theory.

Analogies

Campbell held that the formal structure of a scientific theory consists of a hypothesis and a dictionary. But he also held that it is not sufficient for a theory merely to display the required formal structure. It must, in addition, be associated with an analogy. An acceptable theory exhibits an analogy to a system governed by previously established laws. And these previously established laws are judged to be more familiar, or more adequate, than the laws deduced from the theory. Campbell declared that a theory

always explains laws by showing that if we imagine that the system to which those laws apply consists in some way of other systems to which some other known laws apply, then the laws can be deduced from the theory.[8]

In the kinetic theory of gases, for instance, an analogy is drawn between the molecules of a gas and a swarm of particles. The particles are presumed to obey Newton's laws and to undergo collisions without loss of energy. This analogy played an important role in the historical development of theories about the behaviour of gases. Initially, the positive analogy between particles and molecules was restricted to the properties of motion and elastic impact. No reference was made to other properties that the particles may have. Subsequently, van der Waals extended the theory to account for the behaviour of gases under high pressures. He accomplished this by making certain assumptions about the volume of a particle and the forces existing between particles. These properties initially were part of the neutral analogy between particles and molecules.

Duhem and Campbell both were aware of the heuristic role of analogy in this instance. But for Duhem, to assert a theory is to assert a positive analogy only, whereas for Campbell, to assert a theory is to assert a positive-plus-neutral analogy. For this reason, Duhem described the transition from the original kinetic theory to its modification by van der Waals as the *replacement* of one theory by another, whereas Campbell described the transition as an *extension* of kinetic theory.

Campbell emphasized that the analogy associated with a theory is not merely a heuristic device to facilitate the search for additional laws. On the contrary, the analogy is an essential part of a theory, because it is only in terms of the analogy that a theory can be said to explain a set of laws. Campbell illustrated this point by formulating the following *ad hoc* theory:

The hypothesis consists of the following mathematical propositions:
(1) $u, v, w, \ldots$ are independent variables.
(2) a is a constant for all values of these variables.
(3) b is a constant for all values of these variables.
(4) $c = d$, where c and d are dependent variables.

The dictionary consists of the following propositions:
(1) The assertion that $(c^2 + d^2)a = R$ where R is a positive and rational number, implies the assertion that the (electrical) resistance of some definite piece of pure metal is R.

(2) The assertion that $\dfrac{cd}{b} = T$ implies that the (absolute) temperature of the same piece of pure metal is T.[9]

It may be deduced from the hypothesis that

$$(c^2 + d^2)a = 2ab \left(\frac{cd}{b} \right).$$

According to the dictionary, this theorem is equivalent to the experimental law that the electrical resistance of the piece of pure metal is directly proportional to its absolute temperature.

What is wrong with such a theory? Duhem would say that it fails to achieve economy of representation, and that it is unlikely to have heuristic value. Campbell insisted, however, that this hypothesis-plus-dictionary is not a "theory" at all. The hypothesis and the dictionary have been formulated solely to imply the desired experimental law. But clearly, a particular law, or even a set of laws, may be deduced from indefinitely many sets of premises. The successful deduction of a law from an hypothesis-plus-dictionary is a necessary, but not a sufficient, condition for explaining the law. According to Campbell, it is only when an analogy is drawn to other known laws that a theory explains the laws deducible from it.

Campbell believed this to be true for mathematical theories as well as for mechanical theories. But whereas the analogy for a mechanical theory is explicitly stated and obvious, such is not the case for a mathematical theory. Campbell explained this by pointing out that in a mathematical theory the laws to which the analogy is drawn are the same laws which are deduced from the theory. The analogy is one of mathematical form. The theory from which the experimental laws are deduced is of the same mathematical form as the laws themselves.

Campbell cited Fourier's theory of heat conduction as an example of a mathematical theory. This theory consists of a mathematical equation and a dictionary. The equation is

$$\lambda \left(\frac{\partial^2 \theta}{\partial x^2} + \frac{\partial^2 \theta}{\partial y^2} + \frac{\partial^2 \theta}{\partial z^2} \right) = \rho c \, \frac{\partial \theta}{\partial t}$$

The dictionary stipulates that θ is the absolute temperature, λ the thermal conductivity, ρ the density, c the specific heat, t the time, and x, y, z the spatial co-ordinates of a point in an infinitely long slab of material. Numerous experimental laws about the conduction of heat through finite slabs of various materials can be deduced from this theory. The experimental laws state relations among the same variables and constants as are mentioned in the theory, and the laws share with the theory a common mathematical form. According to Campbell, it is in virtue of this analogy between Fourier's theory and the experimental laws of heat conduction that the theory may be said to explain the laws.

Campbell maintained that the aim of science is the discovery and explanation of laws, and that laws can be explained only by their incorporation in theories. His incisive analysis of the structure of scientific theories was a further blow against inductivist views of scientific procedure.

Mechanical theories, in particular, arise only upon successful application of an analogy. And no rules can be specified in advance to separate appropriate from inappropriate analogies. The imagination of the theorist is restricted only by the requirements of internal consistency and the deducibility of experimental laws. Once formulated, the mark of a successful mechanical theory is its fruitfulness in suggesting further correlations.

Mathematical theories also arise only upon the successful application of analogies. In this process, considerations of mathematical simplicity are important. But Campbell insisted that the formulation of a mathematical theory is not simply an extrapolation of experimental laws. The theorist must select among alternative mathematical relations which both imply the laws and exhibit some similarity of mathematical form to the laws. There is nothing in the experimental laws themselves which forces him to select one particular alternative.[10]

HEMPEL'S CRITICISM OF CAMPBELL'S POSITION ON ANALOGIES

Campbell's claim that it is only in virtue of an analogy that a scientific theory may be said to explain laws deducible from it has been challenged by Carl Hempel. Hempel argued that Campbell's *ad hoc* theory about the electrical resistance of metals does not prove that an appeal to an analogy is essential to scientific explanation.

Hempel suggested a different *ad hoc* theory from which the law of resistance may be deduced. The hypothesis consists of the following two relations:

$$(1)\ c(u) = \frac{k_1 a(u)}{b(u)}, \text{ and } \quad (2)\ d(u) = \frac{k_2 b(u)}{a(u)},$$

where k_1 and k_2 are constants. The dictionary specifies that, for any piece of pure metal u, $c(u)$ is its electrical resistance and $d(u)$ is the reciprocal of its absolute temperature.[11]

It may be deduced from the above hypothesis that

$$c(u) = k_1 k_2 \frac{1}{d(u)}.$$

In terms of the dictionary, this relation stipulates that the electrical resistance of a piece of pure metal is directly proportional to its absolute temperature.

Hempel pointed out that his theory, unlike that of Campbell, does display an analogy to a previously established law. Each of the relations stated in the hypothesis is a formal analogue of Ohm's Law.* But the existence of this analogy adds no explanatory power to the theory. As Duhem had observed, the explanatory power of a theory derives from arguments in which experimental laws are deduced, and analogies are not involved in these arguments. Hempel emphasized that both his own theory and Campbell's alternative theory are deficient in explanatory power because there is just one single experimental law which can be deduced within each theory. Neither theory achieves conceptual integration by showing how a particular set of theoretical assumptions implies a number of different experimental laws. According to Hempel, it is this conceptual integration, which Duhem had called the "representative function", that constitutes the explanatory power of a scientific theory.

Hempel conceded that analogies often are of value in guiding further research. He did not dispute the fact that analogies have been influential in the historical development of the sciences. But he did maintain, with Duhem, that since analogies do not occur as premisses in the deduction of experimental laws, analogies are not part of the structure of scientific theories.

The most that has been established by Hempel's counter-case is that not every appeal to a similarity of form provides an explanation for a set of laws. This leaves unaffected Campbell's claim that the explanation of laws by a theory is achieved only by formulating an analogy to *some* system governed by previously established laws. Campbell presumably would agree that the reference to Ohm's Law does not establish a proper analogue, and that Hempel's hypothesis-plus-dictionary has no explanatory power. But Campbell is committed only to the position that if a theory does have explanatory power, then it exhibits an analogy to a system governed by previously established laws. A "theory" which displays an analogy but which does not have explanatory power is not a counter-case to this claim.

* $i = \dfrac{V}{R}$, where i is the current, V the potential difference, and R the resistance, in an electrical circuit.

HESSE ON THE SCIENTIFIC USE OF ANALOGIES

Mary Hesse has suggested that to use an analogy in science often is to claim that two types of relations hold between an analogue and the system to be explained. The first is similarity relations between the properties of the analogue and the properties of the system to be explained. The second is causal relations, or functional relations, which hold both for the analogue and for the system to be explained. For instance, an analogy between the properties of sound and the properties of light may be represented as follows:

Causal Relations	Properties of Sound	Properties of Light
laws of reflection, refraction, *et al.*	echoes loudness pitch propagated in air ·····	reflection brightness colour propagated in "ether" ·····

similarity
relations

This analogy may be used to make a twofold claim. The first claim is that the corresponding properties in each column are similar. The second claim is that there are causal relations of the same type that link the terms within each column. These would include laws of reflection, refraction, the variation of intensity with distance, and the like. Hesse pointed out that each of these claims may be challenged. One may argue that the similarity relations are superficial. And one may argue that it is inappropriate to apply the known causal relations of sound propagation to the case of light propagation.[12]

The analogy used in Hempel's counter-case differs in an important respect from the sound–light analogy. In the sound–light analogy, horizontal similarity relations are presumed to hold independently of the existence of vertical causal relations. This is not the case in Hempel's analogy. The only relation claimed to hold between terms of the analogue and terms of the system to be explained is participation in functional relationships of the same form. Horizontal relatedness is established only in virtue of an identity of form in the respective vertical relations, viz.:

Functional relations	Properties of electrical circuits		Properties of a piece of pure metal			
			Axiom (1)		Axiom (2)	
① ∝ ②/③	①	i	①	$c(u)$	①	$d(u)$
	②	V	②	$a(u)$	②	$b(u)$
	③	R	③	$b(u)$	③	$a(u)$

Hesse referred to analogies of this type as "formal analogies" to distinguish them from "material analogies" which do have horizontal similarity relations that are independent of vertical relations.[13]

Hesse maintained that the acceptability of formal analogies depends entirely on the appropriateness of the formal relations cited. In Hempel's counter-case, there would seem to be no reason (apart from establishing a deductive relation yielding the known law) to select Ohm's Law as analogue. For the purpose of deducing the known law, the Ideal Gas Law* would be an equally good analogue. We have been given no reason to believe that there is any connection between Hempel's axioms and the flow of current in an electrical circuit. What is needed at this point is a criterion of appropriateness of analogical links.

HARRÉ ON THE IMPORTANCE OF UNDERLYING MECHANISMS

In opposition to the Duhem-Hempel view of theories, R. Harré has recommended a "Copernican Revolution" in which emphasis is shifted from the formal, deductive structure of theories to the associated models. He has declared that

the Copernican revolution in the philosophy of science consists in bringing models into the central position as instruments of thought, and relegating deductively organized structures of propositions to a heuristic role only, and resurrecting the notion of the generation of one event or state of affairs by another. On this view theory construction becomes essentially the building up of ideas of hypothetical mechanisms.[14]

Harré maintained that this emphasis is more consistent with "the persistent intuitions of scientists"[15] than is the position of Duhem.

Harré distinguished three component parts of a scientific theory: statements about a model, empirical laws, and transformation rules. The statements about a model typically include both hypotheses

* $P = k \dfrac{T}{V}$, which also has the form ① ∝ ②/③.

that assert the existence of theoretical entities and hypotheses about the behaviour of these entities. The transformation rules may comprise both causal hypotheses and modal transforms. Causal hypotheses may be expressed in conditional sentences of the form 'If M then E', where 'M' is a state of the model, and 'E' is a type of observed effect. Modal transforms may be expressed in bi-conditional sentences of the form 'M if, and only if, E'.

On this analysis, the structure of the kinetic theory of gases would be represented, in part, as follows:

MODEL	TRANSFORMATION RULES	EMPIRICAL LAWS
Existential hypotheses 'There exist molecules.'	Causal 'Pressure is caused by molecular impacts.' ('If I then P.')	$\dfrac{PV}{T} =$ constant
Descriptive hypotheses 'Collisions are elastic.' '$\triangle m_i v_i =$ constant.'	Modal 'Temperature is the mean kinetic energy of the molecules.' ('T if, and only if, $K.E.$')	....

With respect to the model embedded in theories, Harré emphasized the existential hypotheses suggested by the model rather than the deductive structure which may be developed from the descriptive hypotheses. He insisted that the formulation of existential hypotheses is a "science-extending" operation, and supported this contention by analyses of the historical development of science. It is incontestable that attempts to justify claims about the existence of theoretical entities such as capillaries, radio waves, and neutrinos, have contributed to scientific progress.

Harré indicated the spectrum of possible outcomes of attempts to confirm existential hypotheses. One possibility is that both the demonstrative and the recognitive criteria for the type of entity sought are satisfied. Mendeleef's predictions of the existence of hitherto undiscovered elements is an example. The recognitive criteria which he specified—physical properties, types of compounds formed, et al.—subsequently were shown to be satisfied by Scandium, Gallium, and Germanium. Much the same may be said for hypotheses about the existence of positrons, viruses, and neutrinos.

In other cases, existential hypotheses may be abandoned because demonstrative criteria have not been met. This was the fate of the hypothesis that there exists a planet whose orbit is inside that of Mercury, and also the hypothesis that there exists an ether within which light is propagated.

And in still other cases, existential hypotheses may be abandoned because recognitive criteria have not been met. In such cases, the demonstration-region is found to be occupied by something that does not satisfy the original recognitive criteria. For instance, microscopic investigations of the human heart revealed that it is a continuous muscle, and Galen's hypothesis that there exist pores in the septum through which blood passes, was abandoned.

In some instances, failure to meet recognitive criteria has resulted in recategorization of the theoretical entity in question. This happened in the case of "caloric". Many eighteenth-century scientists explained thermal effects in terms of the transfer of an invisible fluid. But in the nineteenth century, various studies indicated that caloric did not satisfy certain recognitive criteria that should be met by substantive entities. For example, this "substance" largely disappeared in certain processes in which mechanical work is performed. One response of scientists was to reinterpret caloric as a quality of substance—the average kinetic energy of its constituent particles—rather than as a substance itself.

According to Harré, one criterion of the appropriateness of analogical links embedded in a theory is the generation of existential hypotheses from the theory. If no existential hypotheses are suggested by a theory, then the theory does not advance our understanding of the underlying mechanisms of natural processes. Harré declared that

scientific explanation consists in finding or imagining plausible generative mechanisms for the patterns amongst events, for the structures of things, for the generation, growth, decay, or extinction of things and materials, for changes within persisting things and materials.[16]

From this standpoint, the theories which Campbell and Hempel formulated to deduce the variation of electrical resistance with temperature, are wholly inadequate.

REFERENCES

[1] Hermann von Helmholtz, 'On the Origin and Significance of Geometrical Axioms', trans. by E. Atkinson, in *Helmholtz: Popular Scientific Lectures*, ed. by M. Kline (New York: Dover Publications, 1962), 239–47.

[2] Pierre Duhem, *The Aim and Structure of Physical Theory*, trans. by P. Wiener (New York: Atheneum, 1962), 32.

[3] Ibid., 207.

[4] Ibid., 135–6.

[5] Ibid., 199.

[6] N. R. Campbell, *Foundations of Science* (New York: Dover Publications, 1957), 122.

[7] Ibid., 150.

[8] Campbell, *What Is Science?* (New York: Dover Publications, 1952), 96.

[9] Campbell, *Foundations*, 123.

[10] Ibid., 153.

[11] Carl Hempel, *Aspects of Scientific Explanation and Other Essays in the Philosophy of Science* (New York: Free Press, 1965), 444.

[12] Mary Hesse, *Models and Analogies in Science* (Notre Dame: University of Notre Dame Press, 1966), 80–1.

[13] Ibid., 68–9.

[14] R. Harré, *The Principles of Scientific Thinking* (London: Macmillan, 1970), 116.

[15] Ibid., 116.

[16] Ibid., 125.

10

Inductivism *v.* the Hypothetico-Deductive View of Science

JOHN STUART MILL (1806–73) received intensive instruction from his father James Mill, a respected economist, historian, and philosopher. The instruction ranged from Greek, commenced at the age of three, to psychology and economic theory. Mill was associated with the East India Company (1823–58), and was elected to Parliament in 1865, where he worked for woman's suffrage and the reform of land tenure in Ireland. He published numerous books and essays in support of the philosophy of Utilitarianism.

The elder Mill impressed upon his son the importance of collecting and weighing evidence, and John Stuart sought to formulate inductive techniques for assessing the connection between conclusions and evidence. He discovered that implicit in the methodology of the sciences are rules of proof of causal connection. Mill set forth his philosophy of science in *System of Logic* (1843), in which he acknowledged his debt to Herschel and Whewell.

ERNEST NAGEL (1901–) was born in Czechoslovakia, went to the United States in 1911, and has spent nearly all his academic career as Professor of Philosophy at Columbia. Nagel was one of the first American philosophers to take sympathetic account of the work of the Vienna Circle. His book *The Structure of Science* (1960) contains incisive analyses of the logic of scientific explanation, nomic universality, causality, and the structure and cognitive status of theories.

PHILIPP FRANK (1884–1966) received a Ph.D. in physics under Boltzmann at the University of Vienna, and in 1912 was appointed successor to Einstein as Professor of Theoretical Physics at the University of Prague. In 1938 Frank went to Harvard, where he gave courses in physics and the philosophy of science. In addition to making contributions to mathematical physics, Frank wrote widely about the philosophy of science. His discussions of causality, and the various interpretations of quantum mechanics and relativity theory are distinguished by a keen insight into the methodology actually practised by scientists.

MILL'S INDUCTIVISM

INDUCTIVISM is a point of view that emphasizes the importance to science of inductive arguments. In its most inclusive form, it is a thesis about both the context of discovery and the context of justification. With respect to the context of discovery, the inductivist position is that scientific inquiry is a matter of inductive generalization from the results of observations and experiments. With respect to the context of justification, the inductivist position is that a scientific law or theory is justified only if the evidence in its favour conforms to inductive schema.

John Stuart Mill's philosophy of science is an example of the inductivist point of view. Mill made certain extreme claims about the role of inductive arguments both in the discovery of scientific laws and in the subsequent justification of these laws.

Context of Discovery

Mill's Inductive Methods. Mill was an effective propagandist on behalf of certain inductive methods which had been discussed by Duns Scotus, Ockham, Hume, and Herschel, among others. So much so that these methods came to be known as "Mill's Methods" of experimental inquiry. Mill stressed the importance of these methods in the discovery of scientific laws. Indeed, in the course of a debate with Whewell, Mill went so far as to claim that every causal law known to science had been discovered "by processes reducible to one or other of those methods".[1]

Mill discussed four inductive methods.* They may be represented as follows:

	AGREEMENT	
Instance	Antecedent circumstances	Phenomena
1	*ABEF*	*abe*
2	*ACD*	*acd*
3	*ABCE*	*afg*

Therefore it is probable that A is the cause of a.

	DIFFERENCE	
Instance	Antecedent circumstances	Phenomena
1	*ABC*	*a*
2	*BC*	—

Therefore A is an indispensable part of the cause of a.

	CONCOMITANT VARIATIONS	
Instance	Antecedent circumstances	Phenomena
1	A^+ *BC*	a^+b
2	A^0 *BC*	a^0b
3	A^- *BC*	a^-b

Therefore A and a are causally related.

RESIDUES		
Antecedent circumstances		Phenomena
ABC		*abc*
B	is the cause of	*b*
C	is the cause of	*c*

Therefore A is the cause of a.

Mill maintained that the Method of Difference is the most important of the four methods. In his summary statement of this schema, he observed that circumstance A and phenomenon a are causally related only if the two instances differ in one, and only one, circumstance.[2] But if this restriction were enforced, no causal relation could be uncovered by application of the Method of Difference.

---

* Mill also discussed a fifth method, a Joint Method of Agreement and Difference, in which these two methods are combined in a single schema.

The description of two instances involves reference either to different places or to different times, or both. But since there is no reason *a priori* to exclude from the list of circumstances position in space and time, it is not possible that two instances which differ with respect to the occurrence of a phenomenon, differ also in one circumstance only.

A further difficulty is that, in Mill's summary statement of the method, all circumstances are on a par. To explain, for instance, why nitroglycerin exploded on one occasion and not on another, one would have to specify, not only the ways in which the substance was handled, but also the number of clouds in the sky and the extent of sunspot activity. If all circumstances were on a par, one could specify an instance adequately only by describing the state of the entire universe at a particular time.

Mill was aware of this. He conceded that the usefulness of Difference as a method of discovery depends on the assumption that, for any particular inquiry, only a small number of circumstances need be considered. However, he maintained that this assumption itself is justified by experience. Mill claimed that, for a great number of cases, the schema of the Method of Difference is satisfied, even though the inquiry is restricted to a small number of circumstances.

This may be so. But then the discovery of causal relations involves more than a mere specification of values which fit the schema. In order to use this method in scientific inquiry, a hypothesis must be made about which circumstances *could be* relevant to the occurrence of a given phenomenon. And this hypothesis about relevant circumstances must be formulated prior to application of the schema. Hence Mill's claim that application of the Method of Difference is sufficient to uncover causal relations must be rejected. On the other hand, once a supposition has been made that a circumstance is related to a phenomenon, the Method of Difference specifies a valuable technique for testing the supposition by means of controlled experiments.

Mill regarded the Method of Difference to be the most important instrument for discovering causal relations. His claims on behalf of the Method of Agreement were more modest. He maintained that the Method of Agreement is a useful instrument for the discovery of scientific laws. But he acknowledged that this method is subject to important limitations.

One limitation is that the method is effective in the search for causal relations only if an accurate inventory of relevant circumstances has been made. If a relevant circumstance present in each instance is overlooked, application of the Method of Agreement may mislead the investigator. Hence, successful applications of Agreement—like successful applications of Difference—are possible only on the basis of antecedent hypotheses about relevant circumstances.

An additional limitation of the Method of Agreement arises from the possibility that a plurality of causes is at work. Mill acknowledged that a particular type of phenomenon may be the effect of different circumstances on different occasions. In the schema above, for instance, it is possible that B caused a in instances 1 and 3, and that D caused a in instance 2. Because this possibility exists, one may conclude only that it is *probable* that A is the cause of a. Mill noted that it is a function of the theory of probability to estimate the likelihood that a plurality of causes is present, and he pointed out that, for a given correlation, this probability may be decreased by including additional instances in which the circumstances are further varied and yet the correlation remains.

Mill believed that the possibility of a plurality of causes can cast no doubt on the truth of conclusions reached by the Method of Difference. He declared that, for any particular argument by Difference

it is certain that in this instance at least, A was either the cause of a, or an indispensable portion of its cause, even though the cause which produces it in other instances may be altogether different.[3]

But what does it mean to speak of "a cause in this instance"? Mill previously had defined a cause to be a circumstance, or set of circumstances, both invariably and unconditionally followed by an effect of a given type. It would seem that Mill's position in the quotation cited above is that a single application of the Method of Difference can establish that each occurrence of a circumstance must be followed by a corresponding phenomenon. Presumably this is the case in spite of the acknowledged possibility that some other set of circumstances also may be followed by the phenomenon in question. This conclusion about Mill's meaning may be supported by citing Mill's claim that a

plurality of causes . . . not only does not diminish the reliance due to the Method of Difference, but does not even render a greater number of observations or experiments necessary: two instances, the one positive and the other negative, are still sufficient for the most complete and rigorous induction.[4]

W. S. Jevons subsequently pointed out that Mill had made an unjustified leap from a statement about what takes place in a single experiment to a generalization that what takes place in one experiment also will take place in other experiments.[5]

Multiple Causation and the Hypothetico-Deductive Method. It is common practice in historical studies of the philosophy of science to contrast the views of Mill and Whewell. Often Mill is presented as identifying scientific discovery with the application of inductive schema, whereas Whewell is presented as viewing scientific discovery as a free invention of hypotheses.

No doubt Mill did make incautious claims for his inductive methods. The methods certainly are not the sole instruments of discovery in science. But despite the comments that Mill directed against Whewell on this issue, Mill clearly recognized the value of hypothesis—formation in science. It is unfortunate that subsequent writers have overemphasized the incautious claims that Mill made in his debate with Whewell.

In a discussion of multiple causation, for example, Mill greatly restricted the range of applicability of his inductive methods. Instances of multiple causation are instances in which more than one cause is involved in the production of an effect. Mill subdivided cases of multiple causation into two classes: instances in which the various causes continue to produce their own separate effects, and instances in which there is a resultant effect other than the effects that would be produced separately. Mill further subdivided the latter class into instances in which the resultant effect is the "vectorial sum" of the causes present, and instances in which the resultant effect differs in kind from the several effects of the separate causes. See top of opposite page.

Mill held that the "Mutual Coexistence of Separate Effects" may be analysed successfully by the four inductive methods. In addition, he held that the same is true of "Resultant Effects Different in Kind". He noted that in this latter type of situation the investigator may correlate the effect with the presence or absence of circumstances, and then apply the Methods of Agreement and Difference.

Mill believed the situation to be quite different in the case of the

Mill's View of Multiple Causation

"Composition of Causes". This type of multiple causation is not amenable to investigation by the four inductive methods. Mill cited the case of motion caused by two impressed forces. The result is motion along the diagonal of a parallelogram, the sides of which have lengths proportional to the magnitudes of the forces.

The Parallelogram of Forces

There is no question here of conjoined causes giving rise to an effect different in kind from the separate effects of the respective causes. Each separate component cause is fulfilled, but fulfilled in such a way as to produce a reinforcement or cancellation of effects. This is true even in dynamic equilibrium, where the net effect of the forces acting is rest.

An important consideration about the composition of forces is that the contribution of the several forces acting cannot be determined from information about the resultant motion. There are indefinitely many sets of forces which could produce a given resultant motion.

Mill concluded that his inductive methods were unavailing in cases of the Composition of Causes—one cannot proceed inductively from knowledge that a resultant effect has occurred to knowledge of its component causes. For this reason, he recommended that a "Deductive Method" be employed in the investigation of Composite Causation.

Mill outlined a three-stage Deductive Method: (1) the formulation of a set of laws; (2) the deduction of a statement of the resultant effect from a particular combination of these laws; and (3) verification. Mill preferred that each law be induced from a study of the relevant cause acting separately, but he allowed the use of hypotheses not induced from phenomena. Hypotheses are suppositions about causes which may be entertained by a scientist in cases where it is not practical to induce the separate laws.

Mill agreed with Whewell that the use of hypotheses is justified if their deductive consequences agree with observations. However, Mill set very severe requirements for the full verification of hypotheses. He demanded of a verified hypothesis, not only that its deductive consequences agree with observations, but also that no other hypothesis imply the facts to be explained. Mill maintained that the complete verification of a hypothesis requires the exclusion of every possible alternative hypothesis.

Mill held that complete verification is achieved sometimes in science, but he cited just one example—Newton's hypothesis of an inverse-square central force between the sun and the planets. Mill claimed that Newton had shown, not only that the deductive consequences of this hypothesis were in agreement with the observed motions of the planets, but also that no other force law could account for these motions.[6] But neither Mill nor Newton advanced a proof that the alternatives examined exhaust the possible ways of accounting for the motions of the planets.

Mill believed that this was a case of multiple causation in which complete verification had been achieved. However, he was aware of the difficulty of excluding alternative hypotheses, and, in other cases, he was most cautious in assessing the status of hypotheses and theories. He maintained, for instance, that although the wave theory of Young and Fresnel had many confirmed deductive consequences, such confirmation was not tantamount to verification. Mill suggested that at some future time, a theory may be formulated which explains not only the phenomena in his day explained by the wave theory, but also those absorption and emission phenomena not explained by the theory.[7] Consistent with the stringent requirements of his concept of verification, Mill maintained an admirably open-minded attitude toward the theories of his day.

Mill attributed to the Deductive Method an important role in scientific discovery. He declared that to it

the human mind is indebted for its most conspicuous triumphs in the investigation of nature. To it we owe all the theories by which vast and complicated phenomena are embraced under a few simple laws, which, considered as the laws of those great phenomena, could never have been detected by their direct study.[8]

On this point Mill and Whewell were in agreement. Both were convinced that the great Newtonian synthesis was the fruit of a hypothetico-deductive method. This being the case, one must conclude that Mill did not defend an exclusively inductivist position about the context of scientific discovery.

Context of Justification

Although Mill did not reduce scientific inquiry to the application of inductive schema, he did insist that the *justification* of scientific laws is a matter of satisfying inductive schema. He held that it is the function of inductive logic to provide rules for the appraisal of judgements about causal connection. According to Mill, a statement about a causal connection may be justified by showing that the evidence in its favour conforms to specific inductive schema.

Causal Relations and Accidental Relations. Mill maintained that an important goal of science is proof of causal connections. He based his discussion of this goal on an analysis of Hume's position that causal relations are nothing but constant sequential conjunctions of two types of events. Mill recognized that if Hume were correct to equate causal relation and constant conjunction, then all invariable sequences would be on a par. But according to Mill, some invariable sequences are causal and some are not. For instance, the addition of a lump of sodium to a glass of water is the cause of the vigorous production of bubbles in the water. But day is not the cause of night, despite the fact that our experience to date has revealed this sequence to be invariable. Mill therefore distinguished causal sequences from accidental sequences. He insisted that a causal relation is a sequence of events which is *both invariable and unconditional*, thereby allowing for the possibility that some invariable sequences are non-causal.

Mill acknowledged that the distinction between causal and non-causal sequences is of value only if some way can be found to establish that some sequences are unconditional. He suggested that an unconditional sequence is a sequence which not only has been invariable in our past experience, but also will continue to be so, "as long as the present constitution of things endures".[9] He explained that he meant by "the present constitution of things" those "ultimate laws of nature (whatever they may be) as distinguished from the derivative laws and from the collocations".[10]

Mill suggested that the status of an invariable sequence may be decided by considering what would happen if the conditions within which the sequence ordinarily takes place are altered. If these conditions can be altered in a way which is consistent with the "ultimate laws", and if the effect then would fail to occur, then the sequence is a conditioned sequence. In the case of day and night, for example, Mill noted that the relevant conditions of this sequence include the diurnal rotation of the Earth, radiation from the sun, and the absence of intervening opaque bodies. He maintained that, since the failure of any one of these conditions to hold would not violate the ultimate laws of nature, the sequence day–night is a conditioned sequence.

The general usefulness of this approach is severely limited by Mill's failure to specify which laws are the "ultimate laws of nature". Mill did not pursue this approach further. He remained convinced, however, that causal sequences do differ from accidental sequences, and that this difference can be exhibited within experience. What is needed, Mill believed, is a theory of proof which stipulates the form of valid inductive arguments. Such a theory would enable a philosopher of science to determine which generalizations from experience state causal relations.

Upon occasion, Mill extolled all four of his inductive schema as rules of proof of causal connection. In his more cautious moments, however, he restricted the proof of causal connection to those arguments which satisfy the Method of Difference.

Justification of Induction. In order to establish that any argument which has the form of the Method of Difference proves causal connection, Mill would have to show that the connection is both invariable and unconditional. Mill believed that he could do this. However, philosophers of science are in general agreement that Mill failed to prove his case. Mill's arguments to substantiate his claim are based on two premisses, and he failed to establish that either premiss is true.

The first premiss is that the positive and negative instances which fit the schema of Difference differ in just one relevant circumstance. But as noted above, Mill could not establish this. The best he could do was to show that in many cases sequences have been observed to be invariable despite the fact that only a small number of circumstances have been taken into account. But this does not suffice to prove that no further circumstance could be relevant to the occurrence and non-occurrence of the phenomenon.

The second premiss is a principle of universal causation, which stipulates that for every phenomenon there is some one set of antecedent circumstances upon which it is invariably and unconditionally consequent. Mill demanded that the truth of the law of causation be established on empirical grounds, and he acknowledged that, in this demand, he was confronted by a paradox. The paradox is that, if the law of causation is to be proved by experience, then it must be itself the conclusion of an inductive argument. But every inductive argument that proves its conclusion presupposes the truth of the law of causation. Mill conceded that his proof appeared to involve a vicious circle. He recognized that he could not prove the law of causation by an inductive argument using the Method of Difference. To do so would be circular, since the law of causation is needed to justify the Method of Difference itself.

Mill thought that he could avoid closing the circle by means of a thesis about inductive arguments by simple enumeration. He maintained that

the precariousness of the method of simple enumeration is in an inverse ratio to the largeness of the generalization. The process is delusive and insufficient, exactly in proportion as the subject-matter of the observation is special and limited in extent. As the sphere widens, this unscientific method becomes less and less liable to mislead; and the most universal class of truths, the law of causation for instance . . . [is] duly and satisfactorily proved by that method alone.[11]

Thus, whereas the generalization 'all ravens are black' is precarious (remember the discovery of black swans), the generalization 'for every event of a given type there is a set of circumstances upon which it is invariably and unconditionally consequent' is not.

Mill held that the law of causation is a generalization of such breadth that every sequence of events affords a test of its truth. He also held that we do not know a single exception to this law. According to Mill, every seeming exception "sufficiently open to our observation", has been traced either to the absence of an antecedent circumstance ordinarily present, or to the presence of a circumstance ordinarily absent.[12] He concluded that, because every sequence of events is a test of the law of causation, and because every sequence investigated has confirmed the law, the law itself is a necessary truth.

Mill thus claimed to have demonstrated that an inductive argument by simple enumeration from empirical premises proves the law of causation to be a necessary truth. However, Mill's "proof" is not successful. No appeal to experience, to the way things are, proves that things could not be otherwise. Even if Mill could make good on his claim that there never has been a bona fide exception to the law of causation, this would not prove the law to be a necessary truth. And Mill requires that the law of causation be a necessary truth in order to justify his claim that arguments which fit the Method of Difference *prove* causal connections.

THE DEDUCTIVE SCHEMA OF HEMPEL AND OPPENHEIM

Mill's inductivist thesis about the context of justification was challenged at once by Jevons. Jevons outlined a hypothetico-deductive view of scientific procedure, the successive stages of which are: (1) Formulation of a hypothesis in the form of a general law; (2) Deduction of consequences from the law; (3) Comparison of these consequences with what is observed.[13]

Jevons insisted that to justify a general law one must do two things. One must show that it is not inconsistent with other well-confirmed laws. And one must show that its consequences agree with what is observed.[14] But to show that a law has consequences that agree with what is observed is to utilize *deductive* arguments. Jevons thus rejected Mill's claim that the justification of laws is by satisfaction of inductive schema. In so doing, Jevons reaffirmed the emphasis placed on deductive testing by Aristotle, Galileo, Newton, Herschel, and many others.

In a widely influential paper published in 1948, Carl Hempel and

Paul Oppenheim discussed the deductive relationship between universal laws* and statements about phenomena in terms of the following schema:

$$L_1, L_2, \ldots L_r \qquad \text{Universal Laws}$$
$$\underline{C_1, C_2, \ldots C_k} \qquad \text{Statements of Antecedent Conditions}$$
$$\therefore \quad E \qquad\qquad \text{Description of Phenomena}$$

where E is a deductive consequence of premises which include both universal laws and statements about antecedent conditions.[15]

Hempel and Oppenheim maintained that the above schema is applicable to both explanation and prediction. In the case of explanation, one starts with a statement about a phenomenon to be explained, and finds a set of laws and statements of antecedent conditions which imply the statement. Hempel and Oppenheim made the important logical point that statements about phenomena cannot be deduced from universal laws alone. It is necessary to include specific information about antecedent conditions. Antecedent conditions include both the boundary conditions within which the laws are believed to be applicable, and those initial conditions which are realized prior to, or at the same time as, the phenomenon to be explained. In the case of an explanation that invokes Boyle's Law, for instance, antecedent conditions include both the maintenance of constant temperature, and an experimentally-produced variation in pressure or volume.

In the case of prediction, one starts with specific laws and statements of antecedent conditions and deduces a statement about a phenomenon. Hempel and Oppenheim insisted that one criterion of acceptability that a universal law must satisfy is that predictions deduced from it according to this schema agree with observations. Subsequently, Hempel has stressed that the acceptability of a law depends on the quantity, the variety, and the precision of the confirming evidence.[16] Snel's Law,† for example, is more adequately

---

* Universal laws are those laws which can be expressed in the form 'In all cases, if conditions A are realized, then conditions B are realized as well'. Universal laws may be distinguished from statistical laws, many of which may be expressed in the form 'The statistical probability for an event of type A to be also of type B is k'.

† Snel's Law states that $\dfrac{\text{'sin } i}{\sin r} = \text{constant'}$ for any pair of media, where i is the angle of incidence of a light ray, and r is its angle of refraction.

confirmed by precise and comprehensive measurements for various angles and media, than by rough measurements for just one angle of incidence and two media.

NAGEL'S CRITERIA OF NOMIC STATUS

The fact that a sentence of universal form is confirmed in a variety of instances is not sufficient to establish the sentence as an acceptable law. Hempel, Nagel, and others, have pointed out that "accidental" universals, as well as "genuine" or "nomological" universals, can function as premises in deductive confirmation schema. For example, the generalization 'All ravens are black' may be confirmed in numerous instances. And the generalization 'All the coins now in my pocket contain copper' may be confirmed by a chemical analysis of a finite number of coins. But scientists do not accord such generalizations the status of "laws of nature". These examples differ in certain respects from nomological universals such as Snel's Law and Boyle's Law.

Nagel has suggested a number of criteria to distinguish nomological universals from accidental universals. For instance, he excluded from the class of nomological universals those generalizations, the evidence for which coincides with their scope of predication.[17] Application of this criterion would exclude the generalization about the coins in my pocket. This is because the truth of this generalization follows from the truth of a finite set of statements about the composition of a group of coins, together with the truth of the statement that the coins examined are the same coins that were in my pocket at the time in question. Nagel insisted, moreover, that the scope of a nomological universal be open to further augmentation.

Since the generalization about ravens satisfies the above criteria, it would seem that additional criteria of nomic status are required. A further suggestion which Nagel examined is that nomological universals "support" subjunctive conditionals, whereas some accidental universals, at least, do not.[18] Boyle's Law, for example, supports the subjunctive conditional that 'In all instances, if x were a gas whose pressure were doubled at constant temperature, then x would be a gas whose volume is decreased by a factor of two'. But the generalization about the coins in my pocket does not support the subjunctive conditional that 'in all instances, if x were now a coin in my pocket, then x would contain copper'.

To apply this criterion is to make a decision about the cognitive status of a generalization. To claim that a law "supports" a specific contrary-to-fact conditional such as 'if the pressure of this gas had been doubled, then its volume would have been halved' is to express a cognitive attitude toward the law. The claim registers the speaker's belief that if the antecedent of the conditional were true—although as a matter of fact it is not—then the consequent would be true as well.

If the belief is warranted, it is very likely because the law in question has theoretical support in virtue of its relationship to other laws. Nagel listed two types of theoretical support which may indicate nomic status.[19] It may be, for instance, that laws L_1, L_2 and L_3 all are deductive consequences of a particular theory. In this case, evidence which confirms L_2 or L_3 may be said to indirectly confirm L_1. For example, since Boyle's Law, Charles's Law, and Graham's Law of Diffusion all are deductive consequences of the kinetic theory of gases, Boyle's Law is indirectly confirmed by evidence which confirms Charles's Law or Graham's Law. This is one type of theoretical support for a generalization. A second type of theoretical support arises if L_1, together with other well-established assumptions, imply a law L_4 for which there is evidential support. For example, Kepler's Law of Areas may be deduced from Newton's Laws of Motion and information about the masses and velocities of bodies in the solar system. Evidence which supports Kepler's Law indirectly confirms Newton's Laws of Motion.

FRANK ON THE CONFLICT BETWEEN "AGREEMENT WITH OBSERVATIONS" AND "SIMPLICITY"

An important aim of science is to formulate a systematic interpretation of phenomena, and not merely to accumulate unrelated descriptive generalizations. The requirement of indirect evidence is consistent with this aim. Acceptance of this requirement by scientists reflects their judgement that direct confirmation alone is not a sufficient condition of nomic status.

The laws and theories for which there is indirect evidence often are "more simple than" alternative interpretations that are in closer agreement with observational evidence. Philipp Frank has emphasized that "agreement with observations" and "simplicity" are conflicting requirements. He noted that complete agreement with observations could be achieved simply by reporting in summary form the data which has been accumulated.[20] Alternatively, one could ask a mathematician to fit a power expansion to the data. The accuracy of such a fit is limited only by the number of terms the mathematician is permitted to use. But such a procedure would violate aesthetic considerations and heuristic considerations which are affirmed, implicitly at least, by most scientists. Given two competing theories, scientists often prefer the one that they believe to be "mathematically simpler" or "conceptually simpler", even though the other theory is more closely in agreement with observations.

Frank conceded that the concept "simplicity", which is invoked on behalf of aesthetic considerations or heuristic considerations, is a difficult concept to pin down, but he insisted that scientists do appeal to one or another of the various meanings of the concept. According to Frank, the history of science reveals that the most important meaning of 'simplicity' is "fertility". He declared that

if we investigate which theories have actually been preferred because of their simplicity, we find that the decisive reason for acceptance has been neither economic nor aesthetic, but rather what often has been called 'dynamic'. This means that the theory was preferred that proved to make science more 'dynamic', i.e., more fit to expand into unknown territory.[21]

The above brief summary of certain views held by Hempel, Nagel, and Frank, may serve to indicate that contemporary philosophers of science affirm three types of criteria of acceptability for scientific laws and theories. One type of criterion refers to the correspondence between a law or theory and empirical data. A second type of criterion refers to the logical relations that a law or theory may have to other laws or theories. And a third type of criterion refers to the heuristic power, or fertility, of a law or theory. In addition, it certainly is true that extra-scientific considerations have been widely influential. Commitment to religious, philosophical, or political ideologies often has influenced the evaluation of scientific theories.

REFERENCES

[1] J. S. Mill, *System of Logic* (London: Longmans, Green, 1865), vol. I, 480.
[2] Ibid., I, 431.
[3] Ibid., I, 486.
[4] Ibid., I, 486.
[5] W. S. Jevons, *Pure Logic and Other Minor Works* (London: Macmillan, 1890), 295.

[6] Mill, *System of Logic*, II, 11–13.

[7] Ibid., II, 22.

[8] Ibid., I, 518.

[9] Ibid., I, 378.

[10] Ibid., I, 378n.

[11] Ibid., II, 101.

[12] Ibid., II, 103.

[13] W. Stanley Jevons, *The Principles of Science* (New York: Dover Publications, 1958), 265–6.

[14] Ibid., 510–11.

[15] Carl G. Hempel and Paul Oppenheim, 'Studies in the Logic of Explanation', *Phil. Sci.*, XV (1948), 138.

[16] Hempel, *Philosophy of Natural Science* (Englewood Cliffs, N.J.: Prentice-Hall, 1966), 33–6.

[17] Ernest Nagel, *The Structure of Science* (New York: Harcourt, Brace & World, 1961), 62–4.

[18] Ibid., 68–73.

[19] Ibid., 64–5.

[20] Philipp Frank, *Philosophy of Science* (Englewood Cliffs, N.J.: Prentice-Hall, 1957), 353.

[21] Ibid., 352.

11
Mathematical Positivism and Conventionalism

GEORGE BERKELEY (1685–1753) was born in Ireland of English stock. He was educated and later taught at Trinity College, Dublin. A devout Anglican, Berkeley was appointed Dean of Derry in 1724. Shortly thereafter, he sought to found a college in Bermuda, a project which failed for lack of funds. He assumed duties as Bishop of Cloyne in 1734. Berkeley's anti-materialist philosophy is set forth in the *Treatise Concerning the Principles of Human Knowledge* (1710) and *Three Dialogues Between Hylas and Philonous* (1713). His later writings include a critique of Newton's version of the differential calculus (*The Analyst*, 1734), and a positivistic critique of Newton's physics (*De Motu*, 1721).

ERNST MACH (1838–1916) was a Vienna-educated physicist who made contributions to mechanics, acoustics, thermodynamics, and experimental psychology, in addition to the philosophy of science. He crusaded against the intrusion of "metaphysical" interpretations into physics. Against the view that science should seek to describe some "objective reality"—e.g., atoms—behind appearances, Mach insisted that science should aim at an economical description of the relations among phenomena.

HENRI POINCARÉ (1854–1912) was born at Nancy into a distinguished family. His cousin Raymond was President of the French Republic during World War I. Poincaré attended the École des Mines with the intention of becoming a mining engineer, but his interests shifted to pure and applied mathematics. After a brief period at the University of Caen, he joined the faculty of the University of Paris (1881). Poincaré made important contributions to pure mathematics and celestial mechanics. His 1906 paper on the electron anticipated some of the results achieved by Einstein in the Special Theory of Relativity. Poincaré's writings on the philosophy of science—*Science and Hypothesis* (1905) and *The Value of Science* (1907)—emphasized the role of conventions in the formulation of scientific theories.

NORWOOD RUSSELL HANSON (1924–67) followed in the tradition of Whewell and Duhem in seeking to draw conclusions about the philosophy of science from studies of the history of science. He was instrumental in founding a combined department of the History and Philosophy of Science at Indiana University, and subsequently became Professor of Philosophy at Yale. His published works include *Patterns of Discovery* (1958), *The Concept of the Positron* (1963), and *Perception and Discovery* (1969). Hanson's creative work ended prematurely when the plane he was piloting crashed into a hillside outside Ithaca, New York.

BERKELEY'S MATHEMATICAL POSITIVISM

ONE of the early critics of Newton's philosophy of science was George Berkeley, a philosopher who achieved a measure of notoriety for having advanced a number of arguments to prove that "material substances" do not exist. In his criticism of Newton, Berkeley accused Newton of failing to heed his own warnings. Newton had warned that it was one thing to formulate mathematical correlations involving forces, and quite another thing to discover what forces are "in themselves". Berkeley held that Newton was correct to distinguish his mathematical theories of refraction and gravitation from any hypotheses about the "real nature" of light and gravity. What distressed Berkeley was that Newton, under the guise of suggesting "queries", did talk about forces as if they were something more than terms in equations. Berkeley maintained that "forces" in mechanics were analogous to epicycles in astronomy. These mathematical constructions are useful in calculating the motions of bodies.

But according to Berkeley, it is a mistake to attribute to these constructions a real existence in the world.

Berkeley maintained that the entire content of Newtonian mechanics is given in a set of equations, together with the claim that bodies do not move themselves. Berkeley was quite willing to grant Newton's claim that bodies do not have the power of self-movement. But he cautioned that Newton's references to "attractive forces", "cohesive forces", and "dissolutive forces" are apt to mislead the reader. These "forces" are mathematical entities only. Berkeley declared that

mathematical entities have no stable essence in the nature of things; and they depend on the notion of the definer. Whence the same thing can be explained in different ways.[1]

Berkeley thus defended an instrumentalist view of the laws of mechanics. He held that these laws are nothing but computational devices for the description and prediction of phenomena. And he insisted that neither the terms that occur in the laws nor the functional dependencies expressed by the laws need refer to anything that exists in nature. Berkeley maintained, in particular, that we have no knowledge of any referents for such terms as 'attractive force', 'action', and 'impetus'. We know only that particular bodies move in certain ways under certain conditions. Nevertheless, Berkeley conceded that terms such as 'attractive force' and 'impetus' have an important use in mechanics, in virtue of their occurrence in theories which enable us to predict sequences of events.

Berkeley opposed that view of science which likens science to cartography. Scientific laws and theories are not like maps. Each entry on a topographical map designates a feature of the terrain. And the adequacy of a map's representation may be ascertained in a reasonably straightforward way. But it is not the case that each term of a scientific theory must designate an independently knowable object, property, or relation in the universe.

Berkeley's instrumentalist emphasis is consistent with, and perhaps is derived from, his metaphysical thesis that the universe contains only two kinds of entities—ideas and minds. His summary statement of this position is that "to be is to perceive or to be perceived". On this view, minds are the sole causal agents. Forces cannot be causally efficacious.

Moreover, Berkeley urged, no distinction can be enforced between "primary qualities" which are objective properties of bodies, and "secondary qualities" which exist only in the perceptual experience of the subject. Galileo, Descartes, and Newton had accepted the distinction between primary and secondary qualities, and had suggested that extension, position, and motion were primary qualities. Berkeley, however, denied that there are any primary qualities of bodies. He insisted that extension and motion are sensible qualities quite on a par with heat and brightness. Any knowledge that we have about the extension and motion of bodies is given to us in our perceptual experience.

Berkeley held that it is meaningless to talk, as Newton had done, about motions in Absolute Space. Space is not something that exists apart from, and independently of, our perception of bodies. Berkeley pointed out that if there were no bodies in the universe, then there would be no possible way to assign spatial intervals. He concluded that if it is not possible to assign spatial intervals in this situation, then it is meaningless to speak of a "space" devoid of all bodies.

In addition, Berkeley pointed out that if every body save one were annihilated, then no motion could be assigned to this body. This is because all motion is relative. To speak of a body's motion is to speak of its changing relations to other bodies. The motion of a single body within an Absolute Space is inconceivable.

Nor does Newton's bucket experiment establish the existence of Absolute Space. Berkeley correctly observed that the motion of water in the bucket is not a "truly circular motion", since it is compounded, not only of the motion of the bucket, but also of the earth's rotation and revolution around the sun. He concluded that this motion which Newton had cited as rotation with respect to Absolute Space may be referred instead to bodies in the universe other than the bucket.[2]

In the application of his theory of mechanics, Newton was forced to substitute relative spatial intervals for distances in Absolute Space. Berkeley suggested that Newton's references to motions in Absolute Space could be eliminated from physics without in any way impoverishing the discipline. He maintained that, whereas 'attractive force' and 'impetus' are useful mathematical fictions, 'Absolute Space, is a useless fiction and should be eliminated from physics. He recommended that the fixed stars be taken as specifying a reference frame for the description of motions.

MACH'S REFORMULATION OF MECHANICS

In the latter part of the nineteenth century, Ernst Mach developed a critique of Newton's philosophy of science that was strikingly similar to the critique given by Berkeley. Mach shared Berkeley's instrumentalist view of scientific laws and theories. He declared that

it is the object of science to replace, or *save*, experiences, by the reproduction and anticipation of facts in thought.[3]

According to Mach, scientific laws and theories are implicit summaries of facts. They enable us to describe and anticipate phenomena. A good example is Snel's law of refraction. Mach observed that, in nature, there are various instances of refraction, and that the law of refraction is a "compendious rule" for the mental reconstruction of these facts.[4]

Mach suggested a Principle of Economy as a regulative principle for the scientific enterprise. He stated that

science itself . . . may be regarded as a minimal problem, consisting of the completest possible presentment of facts with the *least possible expenditure of thought*.[5]

The scientist should seek to formulate relations that summarize great numbers of facts. Mach stressed that a particularly effective way of achieving economy of representation is the formulation of comprehensive theories in which empirical laws are deduced from a few general principles.

Mach also shared Berkeley's conviction that it is a mistake to assume that the concepts and relations of science correspond to that which exists in nature. He conceded, for instance, that theories about atoms may be useful for the description of certain phenomena, but he insisted that this provides no evidence for the existence of atoms in nature.

Like Berkeley, Mach refused to posit a realm of "reality"—whether of primary qualities, atoms, or electric charges—behind the realm of appearance. His phenomenalism was quite as thorough-going as that of Berkeley. Mach declared that

in the investigation of nature, we have to deal only with knowledge of the connexion of appearances with one another. What we represent to ourselves behind the appearances exists *only* in our understanding, and has for us only the value of a *memoria technica* or formula, whose form, because it is arbitrary and irrelevant, varies very easily with the standpoint of our culture.[6]

Mach sought to reformulate Newtonian mechanics from a phenomenalist standpoint. He hoped to show, by means of this reformulation, that mechanics may be divested of "metaphysical" speculations about motions in Absolute Space and Time. The reformulation took the form of a subdivision of the fundamental propositions of mechanics into two classes—empirical generalizations and *a priori* definitions.

According to Mach, the basic empirical generalizations of mechanics are (1) that

bodies set opposite each other induce in each other, under certain circumstances to be specified by experimental physics, contrary accelerations in the direction of their line of junction;

(2) that the mass-ratio of two bodies is independent of the physical states of the bodies; and (3) that the accelerations which each body $A, B, C, \ldots$ induces in body K are independent of each other.

To these empirical generalizations, Mach added definitions of 'mass-ratio' and 'force'. The 'mass-ratio' of two bodies is "the negative inverse ratio of the mutually induced accelerations of those bodies", and 'force' is the 'product of mass and acceleration'.[7]

Mach regarded the empirical generalizations as contingent truths which are confirmed by experimental evidence. Supposedly, these generalizations would be falsified if the results of experiments turn out to be different than hitherto observed.

Mach emphasized that the generalizations in his reformulation become empirically significant only upon specification of procedures for measuring spatial intervals and temporal intervals. He suggested that spatial intervals be measured relative to a co-ordinate system defined by the "fixed" stars, thereby eliminating all reference to Absolute Space. He also insisted that because it is meaningless to speak of a motion "uniform in itself", references to Absolute Time be eliminated. According to Mach, temporal intervals must be measured by physical processes.

But even if satisfactory physical procedures can be found for determining spatio-temporal intervals, it may be argued that Mach has not established that the empirical generalizations of his reformulation are subject to the possibility of being falsified. The phrase 'under certain circumstances to be specified by experimental physics', which occurs in the first generalization, conceals a problem. The physicist seeks to test the generalization for isolated systems which are unaffected by changes external to the system itself. But failure to record "contrary accelerations in the direction of their line of junction" may be taken to prove, not that the generalization is false, but that the two bodies have been incompletely isolated from disturbing influences. A physicist interested in preserving at all costs the generalization in question could use it as a convention to determine whether a system of bodies qualifies as an isolated system. As a convention, this relation would be subject to neither confirmation nor refutation.

DUHEM ON THE LOGIC OF DISCONFIRMATION

The conventionalist point of view received further support from Pierre Duhem's analysis of what is involved in the disconfirmation of hypotheses. Duhem emphasized that the prediction that a phenomenon will occur is made from a set of premises, and that failure to observe the predicted phenomenon falsifies only the *conjunction* of these premises. Duhem's analysis may be restated in terms of the schema of Hempel and Oppenheim:

$$L_1, L_2, \ldots L_r \qquad \text{General Laws}$$
$$\underline{C_1, C_2, \ldots C_k} \qquad \text{Statements of Antecedent Conditions}$$
$$\therefore E \qquad \text{Description of Phenomena}$$

Observation that E is not the case implies only that the conjunction of the premises is false. And it suffices to make this conjunction false, that any one of the laws, or any one of the antecedent conditions, be false.

Consider a case in which the law 'all blue litmus paper turns red in acid solution' is tested by placing a piece of paper in a liquid. Consistent with the schema, we predict that the paper turns red, viz.:

L For all cases, if a piece of blue litmus paper is placed in an acid solution, then it turns red.

C A piece of blue litmus paper is placed in an acid solution.

$\therefore E$ The piece of paper turns red.

This argument is valid—if the premises are true, then the conclusion must be true as well. Consequently, if the conclusion is false, one or more of the premises must be false. But if the paper does not turn red, what is falsified is the conjunction of L and C, and not L

itself. One may continue to affirm L, by claiming either that there was no blue litmus dye present or that the paper was not placed in an acid solution. Of course, there may be available independent means for ascertaining the truth of the statement about antecedent conditions. But observation that E is not the case does not, in itself, falsify L.

Duhem was interested primarily in more complicated cases in which a number of hypotheses are involved in the prediction that a phenomenon occurs. He emphasized that, even if the antecedent conditions are correctly stated for such cases, failure to observe the predicted phenomenon falsifies only the conjunction of hypotheses. To restore agreement with observations, the scientist is free to alter any one of the hypotheses that occur in the premises. He may decide, for instance, to retain one particular hypothesis as is, and replace or modify the other hypotheses in the set. To adopt such a strategy is to attribute to that one particular hypothesis the status of a convention for which the question of truth or falsity does not arise.

But although Duhem did indicate the way in which a hypothesis might be converted into a nondefeasible convention, he did not draw up a list of specific hypotheses which should be interpreted as nothing but conventions. He believed that, when disconfirming evidence turns up, the decision about which assumptions of a theory are to be modified should be left to the good judgement of scientists. And he indicated that a necessary condition for the exercise of good judgement is a dispassionate, objective attitude.

In some cases, there may be good reasons for making changes in one of the assumptions of a theory rather than another. This would be so, for instance, if one assumption occurs in a number of confirmed theories, whereas a second assumption occurs only in the theory under consideration. But there is nothing in the logic of disconfirmation that pinpoints the erroneous part of the theory.

Duhem applied his analysis of the logic of disconfirmation to the idea of a "crucial experiment". Francis Bacon had suggested that there do exist crucial experiments, or "Instances of the Fingerpost", which conclusively decide the issue between competing theories. In the nineteenth century, it was widely supposed that Foucault's determination that the velocity of light is greater in air than in water was a crucial experiment. The physicist Arago, for instance, claimed that Foucault's experiment demonstrated, not only that light is *not* a stream of emitted particles, but also that light *is* a wave motion.

Duhem pointed out that Arago was wrong on two counts. In the first place, the Foucault experiment falsifies only a set of hypotheses. Within the corpuscular theories of Newton and Laplace, the prediction that light moves faster in water than in air is deduced only from a group of propositions. The emission hypothesis, which likens light to a swarm of projectiles, is but one of these premisses. There are, in addition, propositions about the interactions of the emitted corpuscles and the media through which they travel. Supporters of the corpuscular theory, confronted with Foucault's result, could have decided to retain the emission hypothesis and make adjustments in the other premisses of the corpuscular theory. And in the second place, even if every assumption of the corpuscular theory except the emission hypothesis were known to be true on other grounds, the Foucault experiment still would not prove that light is a wave motion. Neither Arago nor any other scientist could demonstrate that light must be either a stream of emitted corpuscles or a wave motion. There may be a third alternative. Duhem emphasized that an experiment would be "crucial" only if it conclusively eliminated every possible set of explanatory premisses save one. He was correct to insist that there can be no such experiments.[8]

POINCARÉ'S CONVENTIONALISM

It was Henri Poincaré who spelled out most forcefully the implications of a conventionalist view of the general principles of science. Poincaré dissociated Whewell's claim that certain scientific laws come to be *a priori* truths, from the Kantian epistemology to which Whewell appealed to justify the *a priori* status of these laws. For Poincaré, there is no question of the existence of a set of immutable Ideas which somehow invest scientific laws with necessity. Poincaré maintained that the fact that a scientific law is held to be true independently of any appeal to experience merely reflects the implicit decision of scientists to use the law as a convention that specifies the meaning of a scientific concept. If a law is *a priori* true, it is because it has been stated in such a way that no empirical evidence can count against it.

Two Uses of the Laws of Mechanics

The law of inertia, for example, is not subject to straightforward confirmation or refutation by empirical evidence. In Poincaré's formulation, the "generalized inertial principle" specifies that the acceleration of a body depends only on its position, and on the positions and velocities of neighbouring bodies.[9] Poincaré observed that a *decisive* test of this principle would require that, after a certain period of time, each body in the universe reassume the position and velocity it had had at some particular earlier time. But such a test cannot be made. The most that can be accomplished is to examine the behaviour of groups of bodies which are "reasonably isolated" from the remainder of the universe. Needless to say, failure to observe the predicted motions within a supposedly isolated system would not falsify the generalized inertial principle. Discrepancies could be attributed to incomplete isolation of the system. The calculations could be repeated, taking into account the positions and velocities of additional bodies. There is no limit to the number of revisions of this kind that could be made.

Poincaré concluded that the generalized inertial principle may be taken to be a convention which stipulates the meaning of the phrase 'inertial motion'. On this view, 'inertial motion' *means* 'motion of a body such that its acceleration depends only on its position and the positions and velocities of neighbouring bodies'. By definition, any body whose motion is not calculated correctly, from data on its position and the positions and velocities of a set of neighbouring bodies, is not a body in inertial motion.

However, although Poincaré held that the generalized inertial principle can be, and is, used as a convention which implicitly defines the phrase 'inertial motion', he also held that the principle can be used as an empirically significant generalization which holds approximately for "almost isolated" systems. Poincaré made a similar analysis of the cognitive status of Newton's other two laws of motion. On the one hand, these laws function as conventional definitions of 'force' and 'mass'. On the other hand, given procedures for measuring space, time, and force, the laws are generalizations approximately confirmed for "almost isolated" systems.

Thus it would be incorrect to attribute to Poincaré the view that general scientific laws are *nothing but* conventions which define fundamental scientific concepts. These laws do have a legitimate function as conventions, but they also have a legitimate function as empirical generalizations. Commenting on the laws of mechanics, Poincaré declared that they

present themselves to us under two different aspects. On the one hand, they are truths founded on experiment and approximately verified so far as concerns almost isolated systems. On the other hand, they are postulates applicable to the totality of the universe and regarded as rigorously true.[10]

Poincaré noted that, in the course of development of science, certain laws come to display these two aspects. Initially these laws are employed solely as experimental generalizations. For instance, a law might state a relation between terms A and B. Taking note that the relation holds only approximately, scientists may introduce term C which, by definition, has the relation to A which is expressed by the law. The original experimental law now has been subdivided into two parts: an *a priori* principle that states a relation between A and C, and an experimental law that states a relation between B and C.[11]

When implicitly defined by Newton's laws of motion, the terms 'inertial motion', 'force', and 'mass' are terms of the same type as C. Poincaré held that it is a matter of convention that these terms are taken to be defined by Newton's laws. No empirical evidence could prove that the stated relation of terms A and C is false. But this is not to say that the choice of definition is arbitrary. Poincaré insisted that the introduction of conventions into physical theory is justified only if it proves fruitful in subsequent research.[12]

The Choice of a Geometry to Describe "Physical Space"

Poincaré also maintained that it is a matter of convention which pure geometry is employed to describe spatial relations among bodies. However, he predicted that scientists will continue to select euclidean geometry because it is the simplest to apply.

In the nineteenth-century, the mathematician Carl Gauss performed an experiment to confirm the euclidean description of spatial relations. He measured the angular sum of a triangle formed by light rays emitted from distant mountain peaks. Gauss found that, within the limits of accuracy of his surveying equipment, there was no deviation from the euclidean value of 180 degrees.

But even if Gauss had found an appreciable deviation from 180 degrees, this would not have proved that euclidean geometry is inapplicable to spatial relations on the surface of the Earth. Any deviation from the euclidean value could be attributed to a "bending" of the light rays used to make the sightings.

Poincaré called attention to the fact that the application of a pure geometry to experience necessarily involves hypotheses about physical phenomena, such as the propagation of light rays, the properties of measuring rods, and the like. Poincaré emphasized that the application of a pure geometry to experience, like every physical theory, has an abstract component and an empirical component. When a physical geometry is not in agreement with observations, agreement may be restored either by substituting a different pure geometry—a different axiom system—or by modifying the associated physical hypotheses. Poincaré believed that, confronted with such a choice, scientists invariably would choose to modify the physical hypotheses and to retain the more convenient euclidean pure geometry.[13]

But as Hempel has pointed out, in certain cases greater overall simplicity may be achieved by adopting a non-euclidean geometry and retaining unchanged the associated physical hypotheses. According to Hempel, Poincaré was mistaken to restrict considerations of complexity to pure geometries alone. What counts is the complexity of the conjunction of a pure geometry and the associated physical hypotheses.[14]

HANSON ON THE USES OF SCIENTIFIC LAWS

An interesting recent discussion of the cognitive status of scientific laws has been given by N. R. Hanson. Hanson viewed the search for answers to the question "What is *the* cognitive status of a law of nature?" to be misguided. According to Hanson, to ask such a question is rather like asking "What is *the* use of rope?"[15] Hanson affirmed the position defended by Wittgenstein in the *Philosophical Investigations*. Wittgenstein had maintained that ordinarily the meaning of a phrase is its *use* in the language.[16]

Hanson analysed the Newtonian laws of motion from this standpoint, and concluded that these laws have been put to a variety of uses, depending on the purpose at hand. Consider the second law. In the eighteenth century, George Atwood invented a machine to confirm this relation experimentally. He attached a weight of different magnitude to each end of a silk thread, passed the thread over a pulley, and measured the resulting acceleration of the system. He compared this acceleration with the value calculated from Newton's second law, and found good agreement. Atwood certainly believed that he was confirming an empirically significant generalization, despite the fact that a systematic discrepancy between observed and calculated accelerations could be attributed to an error in determining the value of the earth's gravitational constant.

Atwood's experiment is but one of several ways in which the second law may be tested. Another procedure for testing the law is to measure accelerations produced by Hooke's-Law-forces.* A physicist who follows this procedure also uses the second law as an empirically significant generalization.

It may be objected, however, that the second law is used as an empirically significant generalization only as long as experimental evidence and predictions from the law are in agreement. But imagine a case in which observed values and predicted values are not in agreement. Would we judge the second law to be false? It is not likely. We would be more apt to question our experimental procedures for measuring time intervals or Hooke's-Law-forces.

As Mach suggested, we may elect to define 'force' as 'mass times acceleration'. If this procedure is followed, then '$F = ma$' is an *a priori* stipulative definition of 'force', and is subject neither to confirmation nor to refutation by empirical evidence. As Hanson pointed out, there is no question but that physicists have used Newton's second law in this way. A case in point is Mach's reformulation of classical mechanics.

These are but two of the uses to which the expression '$F = ma$' has been put. Hanson noted that the expression also has been used as a schema for making inferences, and as a rule which specifies a technique for measuring forces.[17]

In the process of setting forth the diverse uses of this expression, Hanson emphasized that the cognitive status of an expression must be evaluated with respect to the system of statements of which it is a part. A given sequence of symbols may serve as a definition in one system of statements and as an empirical generalization in a second system of statements. Sentences do not come tagged with labels which read 'empirically significant' or '*a priori* true'. It is only by observing how a sentence is *used* within a particular theoretical system that its cognitive significance can be determined.

---

* Hooke's Law relates the deformation of a body to the force applied.

REFERENCES

1 George Berkeley, 'Of Motion', in *The Works of George Berkeley*, ed. by A. A. Luce and T. E. Jessop, vol. IV (London: Thomas Nelson, 1951), 50.

2 Ibid., 48–9.

3 Ernst Mach, *The Science of Mechanics*, trans. by T. J. McCormack (La Salle: Open Court, 1960), 577.

4 Ibid., 582.

5 Ibid., 586.

6 Mach, *History and Root of the Principle of the Conservation of Energy*, trans. by P. E. B. Jourdain (Chicago: Open Court, 1911), 49.

7 Mach, *The Science of Mechanics*, 303–4.

8 Pierre Duhem, *The Aim and Structure of Physical Theory*, trans. by Philip P. Wiener (New York: Atheneum, 1962), 186–90.

9 Henri Poincaré, *Science and Hypothesis*, trans. by G. B. Halsted (New York: Science Press, 1905), 69.

10 Ibid., 98.

11 Ibid., 100.

12 Poincaré, *The Value of Science*, trans. by G. B. Halsted (New York: Science Press, 1907), 110.

13 Poincaré, *Science and Hypothesis*, 39.

14 Carl Hempel, 'Geometry and Empirical Science', *American Mathematical Monthly*, 52 (1945), 7–17; reprinted in H. Feigl and W. Sellars, eds., *Readings in Philosophical Analysis*, 238–49.

15 N. R. Hanson, *Patterns of Discovery* (Cambridge: Cambridge University Press, 1958), 98.

16 Ludwig Wittgenstein, *Philosophical Investigations*, trans. by G. E. M. Anscombe (New York: Macmillan, 1953), 20.

17 Hanson, *Patterns of Discovery*, 99–112.

12

Twentieth-century Views on the Demarcation of Science

PERCY WILLIAMS BRIDGMAN (1882–1961) was a physicist, a Nobel-prize winner, who conducted pioneering investigations of the properties of matter under high pressures. His experimental determinations included the electrical and thermal properties of various substances at pressures as high as 100,000 atmospheres. In 1939 he closed his high-pressure laboratory at Harvard to visitors from totalitarian countries, an act that produced controversy within the academic community. Bridgman championed a methodological orientation known as operationalism, in which emphasis is placed on operations performed to assign values to scientific concepts.

RUDOLF CARNAP (1891–1970) was a member of the Vienna Circle (1926–1935), who taught subsequently at the University of Chicago and UCLA. His contributions to the philosophy of science include studies on the formal properties of language systems, the definition of scientific concepts, and the structure of scientific theories. In addition, he developed an inductive logic for the estimation of "degree of confirmation" as a relation between hypotheses and sentences stating evidence.

ALFRED J. AYER (1910–) is Wykeham Professor of Logic at Oxford. Ayer was largely responsible for introducing into England the viewpoint of the Vienna Circle. In *Language, Truth, and Logic* (1936), he forcefully applied the verifiability criterion to moral evaluations and to metaphysical and theological claims about that which transcends experience. Subsequently, Ayer has contributed valuable epistemological studies in *The Problem of Knowledge* (1956) and *The Concept of a Person* (1963).

KARL POPPER (1902–   ) is Professor of Logic and Scientific Method at the University of London. In the influential *Logic of Scientific Discovery* (German 1934, English 1959), Popper criticized the Vienna Circle's search for a criterion of empirically meaningful statements, and suggested instead that empirical science be demarcated from pseudoscience with respect to methodology practised. He has reaffirmed and augmented this position in *Conjectures and Refutations* (1963). During World War II, Popper published *The Open Society and its Enemies*, an attack on Plato, Hegel, Marx, and all thinkers who would impose inexorable laws on history.

ARISTOTLE was the first philosopher of science to emphasize the demarcation of scientific interpretations from non-scientific interpretations. He held that this demarcation must be achieved prior to the subdivision of scientific interpretations into those that are acceptable and those that are not.*

Galileo subsequently applied Aristotle's insight to exclude from the domain of science, certain of Aristotle's own interpretations. By restricting scientific interpretations to assertions about primary qualities, Galileo excluded from science interpretations which appeal to "natural motions" toward "natural places".†

In the early part of the twentieth century, a number of scientists and philosophers addressed the problem of demarcation. One important result was the statement of a methodological orientation known as "operationalism".

THE OPERATIONAL CRITERION

Operationalism is a thesis about the demarcation of scientific concepts, a thesis derived, in part, from Newton's insistence that experimental science deal only with properties whose values can be measured. Operationalism often is associated with the writings of P. W. Bridgman. Bridgman claimed only that he had made explicit a methodology already practised by certain scientists—notably Mach, Poincaré, Duhem, and Einstein.

Mach, for instance, in his reformulation of Newtonian mechanics,

* See Chapter I.   † See Chapter VII.

suggested a definition of 'mass' in terms of the results of operations performed. The definition stipulated, in part, that the ratio of two masses is equal to the inverse ratio of the accelerations of the two bodies, observed under specified conditions. Mach stressed that a definition of 'mass' in terms of observed motions, is clearly superior to any purely verbal definition in terms of "quantity of matter".[1] Mach also examined Newton's concepts of Absolute Space and Absolute Time, and concluded that, since no operations can be performed to assign values to these concepts, they should be eliminated from physics.[2]

Poincaré, adopting a similar standpoint, stated the general principle that a concept is useful in science only if we know how to measure its values. For this reason, he criticized the claim that the concept of force is an extrapolation from our direct intuitive apprehension of effort. What counts, according to Poincaré, is not what force is "in itself", but rather knowledge of how to measure it.[3]

Duhem also insisted that scientific concepts be defined with reference to physical operations. He restated Galileo's thesis that the first stage in scientific inquiry is the selection of primary qualities which are subject to operations of measurement. Unlike Galileo, however, Duhem recognized the provisional character of these qualities. He observed that qualities are labelled "primary" only in the service of some theory, and he concluded that in subsequent research they may be broken down into other qualities, or even replaced altogether.[4]

In addition, Duhem extended the operational requirement to scientific theories. He maintained that a theory can be empirically significant only if its conclusions make assertions about concepts whose values can be measured. But he also recognized that not every term of a theory need be linked to measuring operations. Duhem stipulated that the use of intervening variables is legitimate provided that the deductive consequences of the theory, in which these variables are imbedded, are confirmed by experience.

It was Einstein's discussion of the concept of simultaneity, however, which most impressed Bridgman. Bridgman pointed out that prior to Einstein's work, simultaneity was assumed to be an objective property of two or more events. Events A and B were believed to have one and only one of three possible temporal relations: A occurred before B, A occurred after B, or A and B occurred simultaneously.

Einstein asked how a physicist could establish the simultaneity of two events. He noted that any judgement of simultaneity involves measurements of the events by an observer. Such measurement, in turn, presupposes a transfer of information from the events to the observer by means of a signal. But since a transfer of information cannot be instantaneous, judgements about the simultaneous occurrence of two events must depend upon the relative motions of the systems which contain the events and the observers. Given a particular set of motions, observer Smith on system 1 may judge that event A on system 1 and event B on system 2 are simultaneous. Observer Jones on system 2 may judge otherwise. And there is no reason *a priori* to prefer Smith's determination to that of Jones. Einstein concluded that 'simultaneity' is predicated correctly only of a relationship involving two or more events and an observer.

Bridgman's Early Position

Bridgman was greatly impressed by the success of the Theory of Special Relativity, and he resolved to draw from Einstein's achievement an epistemological lesson. One important conclusion of Einstein was that the concept "absolute simultaneity" has no empirical significance. Bridgman suggested as a general principle that all concepts which are not linked to measuring procedures should be excluded from physics. He observed that

if by convention we agree to use only those concepts in describing physical situations to which we can give a meaning in terms of physical operations, then we are sure that we shall not have to retract.[5]

Bridgman acknowledged that the relation between values assigned to a concept and measuring procedures may be complex. He noted, for instance, that the stress within a deformed elastic body is computed via mathematical theory from measurements made of the surface of the body. Nevertheless, stress is a bona fide scientific concept which satisfies the operational criterion of demarcation.[6] Bridgman held that the case is otherwise for Absolute Space, Absolute Time, and the idea that, as the solar system moves through space, both measuring instruments and the dimensions of objects measured contract at the same rate.[7]

In *The Logic of Modern Physics* (1927), Bridgman made a further claim for operational analysis. In addition to formulating an operational criterion of demarcation for scientific concepts, he affirmed an operational theory of meaning. Bridgman claimed that the meaning of a concept is nothing more than the operations performed to assign values to it. He declared that

the concept of length is . . . fixed when the operations by which length is measured are fixed: that is, the concept of length involves as much as and nothing more than the set of operations by which length is determined. In general, we mean by any concept nothing more than a set of operations; *the concept is synonymous with the corresponding set of operations.*[8]

The concept temperature, for example, means nothing more than the operations by which values of temperature are assigned. Hence, "temperature measured by a thermometer" and "temperature measured by a thermocouple" are two distinct concepts.

Bridgman's Revised Position

In his later writings, Bridgman reaffirmed the operational criterion of demarcation for scientific concepts. A bona fide scientific concept must be linked, however indirectly, to measuring procedures. However, he revised his earlier claim that the meaning of a concept is synonymous with operations performed to apply it in specific situations. His later position was that concepts can be said to be synonymous with operations only if we count as "operations" any conscious activities whatsoever. In this broad sense of 'operation', it would be redundant to speak of "operational definitions".

However, the context in which Bridgman's initial statement of the operational theory of meaning had been given was a discussion of instrumental procedures for assigning values to such concepts as length and time. Some critics assumed that Bridgman's early position was that the meaning of an empirically significant concept is the *physical* operations performed in assigning values to it. R. B. Lindsay is one critic who accused Bridgman of defending this position.[9] But a careful reading of Bridgman's discussions in *The Logic of Modern Physics* and *The Nature of Physical Theory* (1936) supports Bridgman's own claim that he never had defended this position. Actually, Bridgman's position on concepts and physical operations was similar to that of Duhem. Bridgman insisted that *some* of the concepts of a theory must be linked to measuring operations. But within a theory that satisfies this criterion of demarcation, he allowed concepts defined only by "pencil and paper operations" which link them to other concepts.

In his later writings, Bridgman also discussed certain inherent limitations of operational analysis. One limitation is that it is not possible to specify all the conditions present when an operation is carried out. But to be of use in science, an operation must be capable of being repeated by any qualified observer. In practice, scientists assume that a particular operation can be repeated independently of the variation of a large number of factors which are taken into account. Whether this assumption is justified is itself a matter of experience. Bridgman noted that in many cases the assumption does seem to be justified, but he cautioned that an extension of formerly useful operations into new domains of experience may force scientists to take account of conditions previously ignored.

A second limitation of operational analysis is the necessity to accept some unanalysed operations. For practical reasons, the analysis of operations in terms of other operations cannot proceed indefinitely. For example, the concept "dissolves" may be analysed in terms of operations which establish uniformity of composition. Such operations may include sampling techniques, and weight and volume determinations. The operation of weighing, in turn, may be analysed further by specifying the methods for constructing and calibrating balances. But such analysis terminates at some point. Scientists usually accept certain types of operations without calling for further analysis. For example, provided that standard precautions about parallax are observed, scientists accept as unanalysed reports of pointer readings on the scales of instruments. To be sure, the instrument may not be functioning properly and the reported value may be incorrect. But the determination of just where the pointer is on a scale is accepted as an operation needing no further analysis. This is true both in classical physics and in relativity physics.

Bridgman observed that our experience to date has been such that no difficulties have arisen from accepting unanalysed this type of operation. He conceded, however, that one day extension of our experience may suggest the need for further analysis. Bridgman was convinced that, although the analysis of operations in terms of other operations must stop somewhere, the decision to accept a particular unanalysed operation is open to challenge. Moreover, he believed that one always can respond to such a challenge by giving a more detailed specification of operations.[10]

The essential claim made for operational analysis in Bridgman's later writings is that it is a useful empirical method. Bridgman believed that theory-construction is facilitated by focusing attention on operations performed in applying concepts in concrete physical situations. Scientists who assume the operational point of view are unlikely to hypostatize their concepts and get bogged down in disputes over the "real nature" of the realities connoted by such concepts as "Absolute Space", "caloric", and "phlogiston". According to Bridgman, the ultimate justification of the operational approach is a pragmatic justification. He declared that

we have observed after much experience that if we want to do certain kinds of things with our concepts, our concepts had better be constructed in certain ways.[11]

THE VERIFIABILITY CRITERION

Bridgman was a practising physicist interested in methodological problems within his discipline. In the early 1920s, a group of philosophers under the leadership of Moritz Schlick approached the problem of demarcation from the standpoint of a different concern. This concern was to purge philosophy of all metaphysics.

The members of the Vienna Circle,* as the group came to be known, believed that they were establishing a turning-point for philosophy. Henceforth philosophy was to be restricted to a clarification of assertions and questions, a clarification which would show that metaphysical disputes are devoid of empirical significance.

Thus began a search for a criterion of empirical meaningfulness that would disqualify metaphysical statements. One proposal was that empirically significant statements are verifiable—a statement is empirically significant if, and only if, it is possible to specify conditions which would make the statement true. It was believed that metaphysical statements could not satisfy this requirement.

A dispute soon arose, however, over the meaning of the phrase 'possibility of verification'. There was general agreement that a statement is empirically significant only if it is logically possible to verify it. This requirement excludes statements such as 'that zebra has black and white stripes and is green all over'. And agreement quickly was reached that mere technical infeasibility does not suffice

* Rudolf Carnap, Herbert Feigl, Philipp Frank, Kurt Gödel, Victor Kraft, Otto Neurath, Moritz Schlick, Friedrich Waismann, et al.

to disqualify a statement. 'There are meteor craters on Pluto' is an empirically meaningful statement, even though we may not at present possess the means to verify it. But there is a third sense of 'possibility of verification'. Reichenbach spoke of the "physical possibility" of verification.[12] According to Reichenbach, it is physically possible to verify a statement only if a verification procedure can be specified which does not violate accepted scientific laws. He suggested that the verifiability criterion be interpreted so that empirical significance be given only to statements for which verification is both logically possible and physically possible. Application of this criterion would exclude, for instance, speculation about the spectrum of a nebula receding from the Earth with a velocity greater than that of light. It is not logically impossible that information be transmitted with a velocity greater than that of light, but we believe it to be physically impossible. Of course, scientists' ideas about physically possible processes do change, and Reichenbach recognized that application of the verifiability criterion is relative to the current state of development of science.

The verifiability criterion soon was recognized to be overly restrictive, however. It excludes universal statements such as 'all sodium samples react with chlorine' and 'all negatively charged bodies attract positively charged bodies'.[13] No finite set of observation reports could establish these statements as true. The most that can be established is that no exceptions have been observed to date. But since many important scientific laws are universal statements of this type, the proposed criterion of demarcation is inadequate.

Nor will it do to require falsifiability instead of verifiability as a sufficient condition of empirical meaningfulness. Falsifiability too is an overly restrictive criterion. It excludes from the range of empirically significant discourse existential statements such as 'there exists at least one binary system of white dwarf stars'. Statements of this type cannot be falsified by any finite set of observation statements which record negative evidence.

Recognition that both the verifiability criterion and the falsifiability criterion exclude statements which ought to qualify as empirically significant, led philosophers to seek alternative approaches to the problem of demarcation. Among these approaches were: (1) to construct an "empiricist language", and require that empirically significant statements be translatable into this language;

(2) to require that empirically significant statements be confirmable, but not verifiable; and (3) to search for a criterion of empirical method rather than a criterion of empirically meaningful statements.

Carnap on Translatability into an Empiricist Language

The first approach was chosen by Rudolf Carnap. Its success depends on the construction of an "empiricist language" into which scientific laws and theories, but not metaphysical statements, can be translated. Carnap constructed an empiricist language which had for its basic empirical vocabulary observational predicates such as 'red' and 'smooth'. However, he soon discovered that statements about many important scientific concepts cannot be translated directly into such a language. For example, whereas the statement-form 'x is an arthropod' may be translated as a conjunction of statement-forms expressible in the empiricist language—'x is an animal', 'x has a segmented body', 'x has jointed legs', etc.[14]—the statement-form 'x is soluble' is not equivalent to 'if x is immersed in a particular liquid, then x dissolves'. This is because it is meaningful to speak of a substance as "soluble" even though at present it is not immersed in a liquid. Moreover, on the material interpretation of 'if . . . then . . .' sentences, the sentence is true whenever its ante-cedent clause is false.* But if 'x is soluble' were equivalent to the above 'if . . . then . . .' statement-form, then any object not pre-sently immersed in the liquid would qualify as "soluble". Both a lump of sugar in a bowl and a silver spoon beside the bowl would be "soluble" in a cup of coffee.

Carnap suggested that, although dispositional properties like 'soluble' cannot be defined explicitly in terms of observation pre-dicates, they can be introduced into the empiricist language by means of "reduction sentences" or "conditional definitions".[15] In the case of 'soluble', the conditional definition might be 'if x is immersed in a liquid, then x is soluble if, and only if, x dissolves'. In general, a dispositional predicate P may be introduced into the empiricist language by the schema 'if operations O are performed,

---

*The truth-table definition of the material conditional relation is:

p	q	$p \supset q$
T	T	T
T	F	F
F	T	T
F	F	T

then P applies if, and only if, results R are observed'. Since P is defined only for those instances in which certain operations are performed, conditional definitions of this type often are referred to as "operational definitions".

An operational definition specifies only a partial meaning for a concept, since the concept is left undefined for cases in which the operation is not performed. Hence dispositional terms like 'temperature', 'electric field strength', and 'response pattern' each may be defined operationally with reference to several types of instrumental procedure. Dispositional properties have an "open texture", and are subject to further specification of meaning as additional operational procedures become available.

This augmented translatability criterion is still too restrictive, however. Certain extremely important scientific concepts can be introduced into an empiricist language neither by explicit definitions nor by operational definitions. Among these concepts are the 'velocity of an individual molecule' in the kinetic theory of gases, and the 'ψ-function' in quantum mechanics. These are theoretical terms which are introduced by the axioms of the respective theories. The axiom systems as a whole are linked to what can be observed by rules of correspondence. In the kinetic theory of gases, rules of correspondence link the root-mean-square velocity of all the molecules to pressure and temperature. And in quantum mechanics, rules of correspondence link the square of the absolute magnitude of the ψ-function (but not ψ itself) to scattering distributions, charge densities, and transition probabilities. But although each axiom system in its entirety is linked to operationally-defined concepts, neither the velocities of individual molecules nor the ψ-function proper is defined in terms of observational predicates. But since these theoretical terms play a vital role in the respective theories, and since the theories as a whole are empirically meaningful, the proposed demarcation must be expanded to include postulationally-defined concepts of this type.

Carnap himself acknowledged this in an essay on theoretical concepts published in 1956. He stated that

empiricists today generally agree that certain criteria previously proposed were too narrow; for example, the requirement that all theoretical terms should be definable on the basis of those of the observation language, and that all theoretical sentences should be translatable into the observation language. We are at present aware that these requirements are too strong because the rules connecting the two languages (which we shall call 'rules of correspondence') can give only a partial interpretation for the theoretical language.[16]

Carnap noted that the translatability criterion must be revised so that statements about theoretical terms qualify as empirically significant. He thus came to recognize three ways in which terms which are not themselves observational predicates may be related to sentences of the empiricist language: by explicit definition, by operational definition, and by postulational definition within a theory. The revised translatability criterion excludes assertions about terms which can be related to observational predicates in no one of these ways.

In the case of a theoretical term, application of the revised translatability criterion requires examination of the entire system of sentences which constitutes the theory. Carnap and Hempel recently have emphasized that, in general, it is only with respect to a group of sentences that it makes sense to ask questions about empirical significance.[17] This position is in marked contrast to the original Vienna Circle position that the empirical significance of individual, isolated sentences could be decided by application of the verifiability criterion.

Ayer on the Deducibility of Observation-Statements

The second approach to demarcation was proposed by A. J. Ayer. It marked a substantial retreat from the original demand for verifiability. To require that an assertion be confirmable is to require only that at least one possible observation report would count as evidence for the assertion. Such a requirement was no innovation in theories of scientific method. Galileo, Newton, and many others, had insisted on it.

But although a requirement of confirmability had been affirmed by numerous writers on the philosophy of science, the logic of its application was not always clear. In the important book *Language, Truth and Logic*, Ayer sought to clarify the logical relationship between empirically significant statements and statements which record observations. Ayer suggested that a statement S is empirically significant if, and only if, some observation-statement O is deducible from the conjunction of S and auxiliary premises P_1, without being deducible from P_1 alone. That is, S is empirically significant if, and only if, there can be found premisses P_i and observation-statement O, such that $\dfrac{S \cdot P_i}{\therefore O}$ is a valid argument, and $\dfrac{P_i}{\therefore O}$ is an invalid argument.[18]

Ayer soon recognized, however, that his proposed Deducibility Criterion was too inclusive. It had been formulated to demarcate empirically significant statements from the claims of speculative metaphysics. But auxiliary premisses P_i can be found which qualify as empirically significant any sentence whatsoever. Consider, as a candidate for empirical significance, the sentence 'Being begets Non-being'. By adding the auxiliary premiss 'If Being begets Non-being, then this pen is green', one may deduce the observation-statement 'this pen is green'. And this observation-statement is not deducible from the auxiliary premiss alone. In general, any arbitrarily selected sentence A satisfies Ayer's criterion of empirical significance, because O may be deduced from the conjunction of A and 'If A then O', but may not be deduced from 'If A then O' alone.

In the second edition of *Language, Truth and Logic*, Ayer revised the Deducibility Criterion in order to overcome this difficulty. He restricted permissible auxiliary hypotheses to the following four classes of statements: (1) analytic statements; (2) observation-statements; (3) statements which, when conjoined with observation-statements O_i, entail a further observation-statement O_j, which statement O_j is not entailed by O_i alone; and (4) statements capable of being established independently as confirmable.[19] An auxiliary premiss such as 'If Being begets Non-being, then this pen is green' presumably would not qualify under any one of these four categories.

Of course, sentences do not come neatly tagged with labels "empirically significant" and "devoid of empirical significance". Moreover, it would be incorrect to regard sentences as tagged with invisible ink, such that the labels become visible upon application of the Revised Deducibility Criterion. Ayer was well aware of this. He emphasized that whether or not a sentence is empirically significant depends on the way in which it is used. For example, the sentence 'Lead melts at 327° C.' may be used either as an empirical generalization about samples of lead, or as an *a priori* definition that specifies a necessary characteristic any substance must have to qualify as lead. In the former usage, a successful melting-point determination confirms the statement. In the latter usage, it does not.*

Ayer pointed out that what starts out as an empirical generalization of the form 'All *A*s have property *P*' may come to be regarded as a partial definition of what it means to be an *A*. In this manner, an empirically meaningful statement may be converted into a tautology. And because this kind of reinterpretation always is possible, Ayer concluded that a demarcation of empirically significant statements must refer to the way in which statements actually are used.

Popper on Falsifiability as a Criterion of Empirical Method

A third approach to the problem of demarcation was chosen by Karl Popper. Popper examined the various unsuccessful attempts which had been made to circumscribe the range of empirically meaningful *statements*, and concluded that these attempts had been misguided. He shared Ayer's conviction that a demarcation of empirically meaningful statements can be effected only with reference to the way in which statements actually are used. For this reason, he shifted the focus of demarcation from statements themselves to the methods employed in confronting them with negative evidence. Popper held that if a system of statements repeatedly is modified in order to explain away negative evidence, then empirical methodology is not being followed. An extreme example of non-empirical methodology would be to defend the generalization 'All patriotic Americans support our country's foreign policy' by insisting that each critic cited as negative evidence is not a *"true patriotic American"*.

According to Popper, proper empirical method is continually to expose an interpretation to the possibility of being falsified. He therefore suggested falsifiability as a criterion of demarcation. But the demarcation thus achieved is between empirical method and the various conventionalist strategies which may be employed to evade falsification. Popper's demarcation does *not* subdivide statements themselves into those which are empirically significant and those which are not.

Popper resolved to take seriously the conventionalist point of view. He noted that it always is possible to achieve agreement between a theoretical system and observational evidence. If certain evidence is

---

* The example is taken from Ernest Nagel, *The Structure of Science*, 199.

inconsistent with consequences of the theory, a number of strategies may be pursued to "save" the theory. The evidence may be rejected outright, or it may be accounted for either by adding auxiliary hypotheses or by modifying the rules of correspondence.[20] These strategies may introduce a staggering degree of complexity into the theoretical system. Nevertheless, evasion of falsifying evidence in these ways always is possible.

Popper concluded that the way to combat conventionalism is to make a decision not to employ its methods. Consistent with this conclusion, he proposed a set of methodological rules for the empirical sciences. The supreme rule is a criterion of adequacy for all other rules, much as Kant's categorical imperative is a criterion of adequacy for moral norms. This supreme rule states that all rules of empirical method

must be designed in such a way that they do not protect any statement in science against falsification.[21]

On the question of adding auxiliary hypotheses to a theory, for instance, Popper suggested that only those hypotheses be admitted which increase the degree of falsifiability of the theory. He contrasted, in this respect, Pauli's exclusion principle, and the Lorentz contraction hypothesis.[22] Pauli's principle was an addition to the Bohr-Sommerfeld theory of the atom. Pauli postulated that no two electrons in a given atom can have the same set of quantum numbers. For example, two electrons in an atom may differ in orbital angular momentum or in spin direction. Addition of this exclusion principle to the then current theory of atomic structure enabled many additional predictions to be made about atomic spectra and chemical combination. The Lorentz contraction hypothesis, on the other hand, did not increase the degree of falsifiability of the ether theory to which it was appended. Lorentz suggested that all bodies on the Earth undergo a minute contraction in the direction of the Earth's motion through the surrounding ether. By means of this hypothesis, he was able to account for the result of the Michelson-Morley experiment. Michelson and Morley had shown that the round-trip velocity of light is the same in all directions on the Earth's surface. This experimental result was inconsistent with the ether theory, according to which the round-trip velocity should be lower in the direction of the Earth's motion through the ether, than in a direction perpendicular to this motion. The Lorentz contraction hypothesis restored agreement between ether theory and experiment, but it did so in an *ad hoc* manner. No further predictions were drawn from the augmented ether theory. Popper cited the Lorentz hypothesis as an auxiliary hypothesis which should be excluded from empirical science by the falsifiability criterion.

Popper viewed the history of science as a sequence of conjectures, refutations, revised conjectures, and additional refutations. And he concluded that the distinguishing characteristic of scientific interpretations is their "susceptibility to revision".[23] He argued that adoption of his proposed rules of empirical method would be consistent with the dynamic, self-correcting nature of scientific inquiry. According to Popper, to insist that scientific interpretations continually be exposed to the possibility of falsification is to promote scientific progress.

REFERENCES

[1] Ernst Mach, *The Science of Mechanics*, 265–71.

[2] Ibid., 271–97.

[3] Henri Poincaré, *Science and Hypothesis*, 73–8.

[4] Pierre Duhem, *The Aim and Structure of Physical Theory*, 128–9.

[5] P. W. Bridgman, *The Nature of Physical Theory* (Princeton: Princeton University Press, 1936), 10.

[6] Bridgman, *The Nature of Physical Theory*, 66; *The Logic of Modern Physics* (New York: Macmillan, 1927), 54–6.

[7] Bridgman, *The Logic of Modern Physics*, 28–9.

[8] Ibid., 5.

[9] R. B. Lindsay, 'A Critique of Operationalism in Physics', *Phil. of Sci.*, 4 (1937), 456.

[10] Bridgman, *The Way Things Are* (Cambridge, Mass: Harvard University Press, 1959), 51.

[11] Bridgman, *Reflections of a Physicist* (New York: Philosophical Library, 1950), 9.

[12] Hans Reichenbach, 'The Verifiability Theory of Meaning', in *Readings in the Philosophy of Science*, ed. by H. Feigl and M. Brodbeck (New York: Appleton-Century-Crofts, 1953), 97.

[13] See, for example, Carl Hempel, 'The Empiricist Criterion of Meaning', in *Logical Positivism*, ed. by A. J. Ayer (Glencoe: Free Press, 1959), 112.

[14] Rudolf Carnap, 'The Elimination of Metaphysics Through Logical Analysis of Language', in *Logical Positivism*, 63.

[15] Carnap, 'Logical Foundations of the Unity of Science', in *International Encyclopedia of Unified Science*, ed. by O. Neurath, R. Carnap, and C. Morris, vol. I, part I, 50–1.

[16] Carnap, 'The Methodological Character of Theoretical Concepts', in

Minnesota Studies in the Philosophy of Science, ed. by H. Feigl and M. Scriven, vol. I (Minneapolis: University of Minnesota Press, 1956), 39.

[17] Carnap, 'The Methodological Character of Theoretical Concepts', 38–76. Hempel, 'Empiricist Criteria of Cognitive Significance: Problems and Changes', in Hempel, *Aspects of Scientific Explanation*, 101–22.

[18] A. J. Ayer, *Language, Truth and Logic* (New York: Dover Publications, 1946), 38–9.

[19] Ibid., 13.

[20] Karl Popper, *The Logic of Scientific Discovery* (New York: Basic Books, 1959), 81.

[21] Ibid., 54.

[22] Ibid., 83.

[23] Ibid., 49.

Select Bibliography

A useful bibliography of sources for the history of the philosophy of science is

LAUDAN, L., 'Theories of Scientific Method from Plato to Mach: A Bibliographical Review', *History of Science* 7 (1969), 1–63.

1. *Aristotle's Philosophy of Science*

WORKS BY ARISTOTLE

The Works of Aristotle Translated into English, ed. by J. A. Smith and W. D. Ross, 12 vols., Oxford: Clarendon Press, 1908–52.

Prior and Posterior Analytics, ed. by W. D. Ross, Oxford: Clarendon Press, 1949. Includes a commentary on these works by Ross.

WORKS ABOUT ARISTOTLE

ALLAN, D. J., *The Philosophy of Aristotle*, 2nd edn., London: Oxford University Press, 1970.

APOSTLE, H., *Aristotle's Philosophy of Mathematics*, Chicago, Ill.: University of Chicago Press, 1952.

GRENE, M., *A Portrait of Aristotle*, Chicago, Ill.: University of Chicago Press, 1963.

RANDALL, J. H., Jr., *Aristotle*, New York: Columbia University Press, 1960.

ROSS, W. D., *Aristotle*, 5th edn., revised, London: Methuen, 1949.

SOLMSEN, F., *Aristotle's System of the Physical World*, Ithaca, N.Y.: Cornell University Press, 1960.

ANSCOMBE, G. E. M., 'Aristotle: The Search for Substance', in Anscombe and Geach, *Three Philosophers*, Oxford: Blackwell, 1961.

DEMOS, R., 'The Structure of Substance According to Aristotle', *Phil. and Phenom. Res.* 5 (1944–5), 255–68.

EVANS, M. G., 'Causality and Explanation in the Logic of Aristotle', *Phil. and Phenom. Res.* 19 (1958–9), 466–85.

LEE, H. D. P., 'Geometrical Methods and Aristotle's Account of First Principles', *Class. Quart.* 29 (1935), 113–24.

McKEON, R. P., 'Aristotle's Conception of the Development and the Nature of Scientific Method', *J. Hist. Ideas*, 8 (1947), 3–44.

SELLARS, W., 'Substance and Form in Aristotle', *J. Phil.* 54 (1957), 688–99.

2. *The Pythagorean Orientation*

GUTHRIE, W. K. C., *A History of Greek Philosophy*, vol. 1, Cambridge: Cambridge University Press, 1962.

HARRÉ, R., *The Anticipation of Nature*, London: Hutchinson, 1965. Chapter 4, 'The Pythagorean Principles', is an analysis of the Pythagorean orientation.

PHILIP, J. A., *Pythagoras and Early Pythagoreanism*, Toronto, Ont.: University of Toronto Press, 1966.

CORNFORD, F. M., *Plato's Cosmology*, New York: Liberal Arts Press, 1957. A translation of Plato's *Timaeus* with running commentary by Cornford.

PTOLEMY, C., *The Almagest*, trans. by C. Taliaferro, in vol. 16 of Great Books of the Western World, Chicago, Ill.: Encyclopaedia Britannica, 1952.

3. *The Ideal of Deductive Systematization*

EUCLID, *Elements*, ed. by T. L. Heath, 3 vols. New York: Dover Publications, 1926.

The Works of Archimedes with The Method of Archimedes, ed. by T. L. Heath, New York: Dover Publications, reprint of 1912 Cambridge University Press publication.

DIJKSTERHUIS, E. J., *Archimedes*, trans. by C. Dikshoorn, Copenhagen: E. Munksgaard, 1956.

5. *Affirmation and Development of Aristotle's Method in the Medieval Period*

GENERAL WORKS ON THE MEDIEVAL PERIOD

CLAGETT, M., *The Science of Mechanics in the Middle Ages*, Madison: University of Wisconsin Press, 1959.

CROMBIE, A. C., *Robert Grosseteste and the Origins of Experimental Science (1100–1700)*, Oxford: Clarendon Press, 1962. Contains an extensive bibliography.

SHAPIRO, H., ed., *Medieval Philosophy, Selected Readings, from Augustine to Buridan*, New York: The Modern Library, 1964.

SHARP, D. E., *Franciscan Philosophy at Oxford in the Thirteenth Century*, New York: Russell & Russell, 1964.

THORNDIKE, L., *A History of Magic and Experimental Science*, vol. 2, New York: Macmillan, 1923.

WEINBERG, J. R., *A Short History of Medieval Philosophy*, Princeton, N.J.: Princeton University Press, 1964.

MOODY, E. A., 'Empiricism and Metaphysics in Medieval Philosophy', *Phil. Rev.* 67 (1958), 145–63.

WEINBERG, J. R., 'Historical Remarks on Some Medieval Views of Induction', in J. R. Weinberg, *Abstraction, Relation, and Induction*, Madison: University of Wisconsin Press, 1965, 121–53.

196   SELECT BIBLIOGRAPHY

ROBERT GROSSETESTE

CROMBIE, A. C., 'Grosseteste's Position in the History of Science', in *Robert Grosseteste*, ed. by D. A. Callus, Oxford: Clarendon Press, 1955.
CROMBIE, A. C., 'Quantification in Medieval Physics', *Isis*, 52 (1961), 143–60.
DALES, R. C., 'Robert Grosseteste's Scientific Works', *Isis*, 52 (1961), 381–402.

ROGER BACON

The Opus Majus, trans. by R. B. Burke, New York: Russell & Russell, 1962.
EASTON, S. C., *Roger Bacon and His Search for a Universal Science*, New York: Columbia University Press, 1952.
STEELE, R., 'Roger Bacon and the State of Science in the Thirteenth Century', in *Studies in the History and Method of Science*, ed. by C. Singer. Oxford: Clarendon Press, 1921, vol. II, 121–50.

JOHN DUNS SCOTUS

Duns Scotus: Philosophical Writings, ed. and trans. by A. B. Wolter, Edinburgh: Nelson, 1962.
BOLER, J. F., *Charles Peirce and Scholastic Realism*, Seattle: University of Washington Press, 1963, 37–62.
HARRIS, C. R. S., *Duns Scotus* (1927), 2 vols., New York: Humanities Press, 1959.

WILLIAM OF OCKHAM

Ockham: Philosophical Writings, ed. with an introduction by P. Boehner, Edinburgh: Nelson, 1962. Contains a bibliography of Ockham's works.
Ockham: Studies and Selections, ed. with an introduction by S. C. Tornay, La Salle, Ill.: Open Court Publishing Co., 1938.
BOEHNER, P., *Collected Articles on Ockham*, ed. by E. M. Buytaert, St. Bonaventure, N.Y.: Franciscan Institute Publications, 1958.
MOODY, E. A., *The Logic of William of Ockham*, New York: Russell & Russell, 1965.
SHAPIRO, H., *Motion, Time and Place According to William Ockham*, St. Bonaventure, N.Y.: Franciscan Institute Publications, 1957.
MOODY, E. A., 'Ockham, Buridan, and Nicolaus of Autrecourt', *Franciscan Stud.* 7 (1947), 115–46.
PEGIS, A. C., 'Some Recent Interpretations of Ockham', *Speculum*, 23 (1948), 452–63.

NICOLAUS OF AUTRECOURT

'First and Second Letters to Bernard of Arezzo', in *Medieval Philosophy*, ed. by H. Shapiro, 510–27.

WEINBERG, J. R., *Nicolaus of Autrecourt: A Study in Fourteenth-Century Thought*, Princeton, N.J.: Princeton University Press, 1948.

6. *The Debate Over Saving the Appearances*

Ptolemy, Copernicus, Kepler, vol. 16 of Great Books of the Western World, Chicago: Encyclopaedia Britannica, 1952. Contains
Ptolemy, *The Almagest*, trans. by R. C. Taliaferro;
Copernicus, *On the Revolutions of the Heavenly Spheres*, trans. by C. G. Wallis;
Kepler, *Epitome of Copernican Astronomy*, Books IV and V, trans. by C. G. Wallis; and
Kepler, *The Harmonies of the World*, Book V, trans. by C. G. Wallis.
Three Copernican Treatises, 2nd. edn., trans. by E. Rosen, New York: Dover Publications, 1959. Contains
Copernicus, *Commentariolis*;
Copernicus, *Letter Against Werner*;
Rheticus, *Narratio Prima*; and
Annotated Copernicus Bibliography (1939–58), compiled by Rosen.
DUHEM, P., *To Save the Phenomena*, trans. by E. Doland and C. Maschler, Chicago, Ill.: University of Chicago Press, 1969.
KUHN, T. S., *The Copernican Revolution*, New York: Random House, 1957.
O'NEIL, W. M., *Fact and Theory*, Part 2, Sydney, N.S.W.: Sydney University Press, 1969.

7. *The Seventeenth-Century Attack on Aristotelian Philosophy*

I. Galileo

WORKS BY GALILEO

The Assayer, trans. by S. Drake, in *The Controversy on the Comets of 1618*, trans. by S. Drake and C. D. O'Malley, Philadelphia: University of Pennsylvania Press, 1960, 151–336.
Dialogue Concerning the Two Chief World Systems (1632), trans. by S. Drake, Berkeley: University of California Press, 1953.
Dialogues Concerning Two New Sciences (1638), trans. by H. Crew and A. de Salvio, New York: Dover Publications, reprint of 1914 Macmillan edition.
Discoveries and Opinions of Galileo, trans. by S. Drake, Garden City, N.Y.: Doubleday Anchor Books, 1957. [Includes *The Starry Messenger* (1610), *Letters on Sunspots* (1613), *Letter to the Grand Duchess Christina* (1615), and a portion of *The Assayer* (1623).]

WORKS ABOUT GALILEO

DE SANTILLANA, G., *The Crime of Galileo*, Chicago, Ill.: University of Chicago Press, 1963.

SEEGER, R. J., *Men of Physics: Galileo Galilei, His Life and Works*, New York: Pergamon Press, 1966.

KOYRÉ, A., 'Galileo and Plato', *J. Hist. Ideas*, 4, (1943), 400–28.

KOYRÉ, A., 'Galileo and the Scientific Revolution of the Seventeenth Century', *Phil. Rev.* 52, (1943), 333–48.

KOYRÉ, A., 'An Experiment in Measurement', *Proc. Am. Phil. Soc.* 97 (1953), 222–37.

MOODY, E. A., 'Galileo and Avempace', *J. Hist. Ideas*, 12 (1951), 163–93; 375–422.

OLSCHKI, L., 'Galileo's Philosophy of Science', *Phil. Rev.* 52 (1943), 349–65.

SETTLE, T. B., 'An Experiment in the History of Science', *Science*, 133 (6 Jan. 1961), 19–23.

WIENER, P. P., 'The Tradition Behind Galileo's Methodology', *Osiris, I* (1936), 733–44.

GEYMONAT, L., *Galileo Galilei*, trans. by S. Drake, New York: McGraw-Hill, 1965.

MCMULLIN, E. (ed.), *Galileo, Man of Science*, New York: Basic Books, 1967.

7. *The Seventeenth-Century Attack on Aristotelian Philosophy*
II. Francis Bacon

WORKS BY FRANCIS BACON

The Works of Francis Bacon, 14 vols., ed. by J. Spedding, R. L. Ellis, and D. D. Heath, New York: Hurd and Houghton, 1869.

WORKS ABOUT FRANCIS BACON

ANDERSON, F. H., *The Philosophy of Francis Bacon*, Chicago, Ill.: University of Chicago Press, 1948.

BROAD, C. D., *The Philosophy of Francis Bacon*, Cambridge: Cambridge University Press, 1926.

FARRINGTON, B., *Francis Bacon: Philosopher of Industrial Science*, New York: Schuman, 1949.

FARRINGTON, B., *The Philosophy of Francis Bacon. An Essay on its Development from 1603 to 1609 with New Translations of Fundamental Texts*. Liverpool: Liverpool University Press, 1964.

ROSSI, P., *Francis Bacon: From Magic to Science*, trans. by S. Rabinovitch, London: Routledge & Kegan Paul, 1968.

TAYLOR, A. E., 'Francis Bacon', *Proc. Brit. Acad.* 12 (1926), 273–94. Reprinted by Oxford University Press, 1927.

DUCASSE, C. J., 'Francis Bacon's Philosophy of Science', in R. M. Blake, C. J. Ducasse, and E. H. Madden, *Theories of Scientific Method: The Renaissance Through the Nineteenth Century*, Seattle: The University of Washington Press, 1960.

PRIMACK, M., 'Outline of a Reinterpretation of Francis Bacon's Philosophy', *J. Hist. Phil.* 5 (1967), 123–32.

7. *The Seventeenth-Century Attack on Aristotelian Philosophy*

III. Descartes

WORKS BY DESCARTES

Oeuvres de Descartes, ed. by C. Adam and P. Tannery, Paris: Léopold Cerf, 1897–1913.
Descartes: Philosophical Writings, ed. and trans. by G. E. M. Anscombe and P. T. Geach. Edinburgh: Nelson, 1954.
The Philosophical Works of Descartes, trans. by E. S. Haldane and G. R. T. Ross, 2 vols., New York: Dover Publications, 1955.
Descartes: Philosophical Letters, trans. and ed. by A. Kenny, Oxford: Clarendon Press, 1970.

WORKS ABOUT DESCARTES

SEBBA, G., *Bibliographia Cartesiana. A Critical Guide to the Descartes Literature (1800–1960)*, The Hague: Martinus Nijhoff, 1964.
Descartes, A Collection of Critical Essays, ed. by W. Doney, Garden City, N.Y.: Doubleday, 1967. Contains an extensive bibliography of articles in English.
Meta—Meditations: Studies in Descartes, ed. by A. Sesonske and N. Fleming, Belmont, Calif.: Wadsworth, 1965.
BECK, L. J., *The Method of Descartes, A Study of the Regulae*, Oxford: Clarendon Press, 1952.
BECK, L. J., *The Metaphysics of Descartes, A Study of the Meditations*, Oxford Clarendon Press, 1965.
SMITH, N. K., *New Studies in the Philosophy of Descartes*, New York: Russell & Russell, 1966.
POPKIN, R. H., *The History of Scepticism from Erasmus to Descartes*, New York: Harper Torchbooks, 1968.
VARTANIAN, A., *Diderot and Descartes*, Princeton, N.J.: Princeton University Press, 1953.
AYER, A. J., 'Cogito ergo sum', *Analysis*, 14 (1953), 27–31.
BLAKE, R. M., 'The Role of Experience in Descartes' Theory of Method', *Phil. Rev.* 38 (1929), 125–43; 201–18. Reprinted in R. M. Blake, C. J. Ducasse, and E. H. Madden, *Theories of Scientific Method: The Renaissance Through the Nineteenth Century*, Seattle: University of Washington Press, 1960.
BUCHDAHL, G., 'The Relevance of Descartes's Philosophy for Modern Philosophy of Science', *Brit. J. Hist. Sci.* 1 (1963), 227–49.
HINTIKKA, J., 'Cogito, ergo sum: Inference or Performance?', *Phil. Rev.* 71 (1962), 3–32. Reprinted in *Meta-Meditations: Studies in Descartes*, 50–76. Reprinted also in *Descartes, A Collection of Critical Essays*, 108–39.
MILLER, L. G., 'Descartes, Mathematics, and God', *Phil. Rev.* 66 (1957), 451–65. Reprinted in *Meta-Meditations: Studies in Descartes*, 37–49.

PASSMORE, J. A., 'William Harvey and the Philosophy of Science', *Australasian J. Phil.* 36 (1958), 85–94.

SUPPES, P., 'Descartes and the Problem of Action at a Distance', *J. Hist. Ideas*, 15 (1954), 146–52.

8. *Newton's Axiomatic Method*

WORKS BY NEWTON

Unpublished Scientific Papers of Isaac Newton, ed. and trans. by A. R. Hall and M. B. Hall, Cambridge: Cambridge University Press, 1962.

Isaac Newton's Papers and Letters on Natural Philosophy, ed. by I. B. Cohen, Cambridge, Mass.: Harvard University Press, 1958.

Opticks, 4th edn. (1730), New York: Dover Publications, 1952.

Mathematical Principles of Natural Philosophy and His System of the World, trans. by A. Motte (1729), revised by F. Cajori, 2 vols., Berkeley: University of California Press, 1962.

WORKS ABOUT NEWTON

BUTTS, R. E. and DAVIS, J. W., eds., *The Methodological Heritage of Newton*, Toronto, Ont.: University of Toronto Press, 1970. A collection of critical essays.

The Texas Quarterly, vol. 10, no. 3 (Autumn 1967), Austin: University of Texas Press. Contains articles on Newton by I. B. Cohen, A. R. Hall and M. B. Hall, J. Herivel, R. S. Westfall, *et al.*

COHEN, I. B., *Franklin and Newton*, Cambridge, Mass.: Harvard University Press, 1966.

DIJKSTERHUIS, E. J., *The Mechanization of the World Picture*, trans. by C. Dikshoorn, Oxford: Clarendon Press, 1961. Contains an excellent discussion of Newton's physics and philosophy of science.

HESSE, M., *Forces and Fields*, Totowa, N.J.: Littlefield, Adams & Co., 1965. Chapter 6 is a discussion of philosophical problems of Newton's physics.

JAMMER, M., *Concepts of Force*, Cambridge, Mass.: Harvard University Press, 1957. *Concepts of Space*, Cambridge, Mass.: Harvard University Press, 1954. Contains analyses of Newton's concepts of force and space.

KOYRÉ, A., *Newtonian Studies*, Cambridge, Mass.: Harvard University Press, 1965.

LEYDEN, W. VON, *Seventeenth-Century Metaphysics*, London: Duckworth, 1968, Chapter 12.

MANUEL, F. E., *A Portrait of Isaac Newton*, Cambridge, Mass.: Harvard University Press, 1968.

WESTFALL, R. S., *Forces in Newton's Physics*, London: Macdonald, 1971.

BLAKE, R. M. 'Isaac Newton and the Hypothetico-Deductive Method' in R. M. Blake, C. J. Ducasse, and E. H. Madden, *Theories of Scientific Method: The Renaissance Through the Nineteenth Century*, 119–43.

BOAS, M. and HALL, A. R., 'Newton's "Mechanical Principles" ', *J. Hist. Ideas*, 20 (1959), 167–78.

BUCHDAHL, G., 'Science and Logic: Some Thoughts on Newton's Second Law of Motion in Classical Mechanics', *Brit. J. Phil. Sci.* 2 (1951–2), 217–35.

COHEN, I. B., 'Newton in the Light of Recent Scholarship', *Isis*, 51 (1960), 489–514.

STRONG, E. W., 'Newton's "Mathematical Way" ', *J. Hist. Ideas*, 12 (1951), 90–110.

TOULMIN, S., 'Criticism in the History of Science: Newton on Absolute Space, Time, and Motion', *Phil. Rev.* 68 (1959), 1–29, 203–27.

9. *Analyses of the Implications of the New Science for a Theory of Scientific Method*

I. The Cognitive Status of Scientific Laws

GENERAL

BUCHDAHL, G., *Metaphysics and the Philosophy of Science*, Oxford: Blackwell, 1969.

WORKS BY LOCKE

Works of John Locke, 10th edn., 10 vols., London: J. Johnson, 1801.

An Essay Concerning Human Understanding, 1st edn., (1690), 2 vols., New York: Dover Publications, 1959.

WORKS ABOUT LOCKE

Locke and Berkeley, ed. by C. B. Martin and D. M. Armstrong, Garden City, N.Y.: Doubleday & Company, 1968. A Collection of Critical Essays.

AARON, R. I., *John Locke*, 2nd edn., Oxford: Clarendon Press, 1955.

GIBSON, J., *Locke's Theory of Knowledge*, Cambridge: Cambridge University Press, 1917.

MANDELBAUM, M., *Philosophy, Science and Sense Perception. Historical and Critical Studies*, Baltimore, Md.: Johns Hopkins Press, 1964, Chap. 1.

O'CONNOR, D. J., *John Locke*, New York: Dover Publications, 1967.

YOLTON, J. W., *John Locke and the Way of Ideas*, Oxford: Clarendon Press, 1956.

YOLTON, J. W., *Locke and the Compass of Human Understanding*, Cambridge: Cambridge University Press, 1970.

LAUDAN, L., 'The Nature and Sources of Locke's Views on Hypotheses', *J. Hist. Ideas*, 28 (1967), 211–23.

YOST, R. M., 'Locke's Rejection of Hypotheses About Sub-Microscopic Events', *J. Hist. Ideas*, 12 (1951), 111–30.

WORKS BY LEIBNIZ

Opera Philosophica, ed. by J. E. Erdman, 2 vols., Berlin, 1840.

Leibniz Selections, ed. by P. Wiener, New York: Charles Scribner's Sons, 1951.

The Leibniz–Clarke Correspondence, ed. by H. G. Alexander, Manchester: Manchester University Press, 1956.
Leibniz. Philosophical Papers and Letters, trans. and ed. by L. E. Loemker, Dordrecht: D. Reidel Publishing Co., 1969. Contains an extensive bibliography.

WORKS ABOUT LEIBNIZ

JOSEPH, H. W. B., *Lectures on the Philosophy of Leibniz*, Oxford: Clarendon Press, 1949.
MARTIN, G., *Leibniz: Logic and Metaphysics*, trans. by K. J. Northcott and P. J. Lucas, Manchester: Manchester University Press, 1964.
RESCHER, N., *The Philosophy of Leibniz*, Englewood Cliffs, N.J.: Prentice-Hall, 1967.
RUSSELL, B., *A Critical Exposition of the Philosophy of Leibniz*, 2nd edn., London: George Allen & Unwin, 1937.
GALE, GEORGE, 'The Physical Theory of Leibniz', *Studia Leibnitiana II*, 2 (1970), 114–27.

WORKS BY HUME

Hume's Philosophical Works, ed. by T. H. Green and T. H. Grose, 4 vols., London: Longmans, 1874–5.
An Enquiry Concerning Human Understanding (1748), Chicago, Ill.: Open Court Publishing Co., 1927.
A Treatise of Human Nature (1739–40), ed. by L. A. Selby-Bigge, Oxford: Clarendon Press, 1965.

WORKS ABOUT HUME

JESSOP, T. E., *Bibliography of David Hume and of Scottish Philosophy from Francis Hutcheson to Lord Balfour* (1938), New York: Russell & Russell, 1966.
Human Understanding. Studies in the Philosophy of David Hume, ed. by A. Sesonske and N. Fleming, Belmont, Calif.: Wadsworth Publishing Company, 1965. A Collection of Essays on Hume's Philosophy.
Hume, ed. by V. C. Chappell, Garden City, N.Y.: Doubleday & Company, 1966. A Collection of Critical Essays.
FLEW, A., *Hume's Philosophy of Belief*, New York: Humanities Press, 1961.
PRICE, H. H., *Hume's Theory of the External World*, Oxford: Clarendon Press, 1940.
SMITH, N. K., *The Philosophy of David Hume*, London: Macmillan, 1941.
MOORE, G. E., 'Hume's Philosophy', in *Philosophical Studies*, New York: Harcourt, Brace & Co., 1922. Reprinted in *Readings in Philosophical Analysis*, ed. by H. Feigl and W. Sellars, New York: Appleton-Century-Crofts, 1949, 351–63.
WILL, F. L., 'Will the Future Be Like the Past?', *Mind*, 56 (1947), 332–47.
YOLTON, J. W., 'The Concept of Experience in Locke and Hume', *J. Hist. Phil.* 1 (1963), 53–72.

WORKS BY KANT

Kant's Gesammelte Schriften, edited under the supervision of the Berlin Academy of Sciences, 23 vols., Berlin 1902.

Immanuel Kant's 'Critique of Pure Reason', trans. by F. M. Müller, 2nd edn. (1896), New York: Macmillan, 1934.

Kant's Kritik of Judgment, trans. by J. H. Bernard, London: Macmillan, 1892.

Metaphysical Foundations of Natural Science, trans. by J. Ellington, Indianapolis, Ind.: Bobbs-Merrill, 1970.

WORKS ABOUT KANT

The Heritage of Kant, ed. by G. T. Whitney and D. F. Bowers, Princeton, N.J.: Princeton University Press, 1939. A Collection of Essays on Kant's Philosophy.

Kant, ed. by R. P. Wolff, Garden City, N.Y.: Doubleday & Co., 1967. A Collection of Critical Essays.

Kant: Disputed Questions, ed. by M. S. Gram, Chicago, Ill.: Quadrangle Books, 1967. A Collection of Essays on Kant's Philosophy.

BECK, L. W., *Studies in the Philosophy of Kant*, Indianapolis, Ind.: Bobbs-Merrill, 1965.

BENNETT, J. F., *Kant's Analytic*, Cambridge: Cambridge University Press, 1966.

BIRD, G., *Kant's Theory of Knowledge*, New York: Humanities Press, 1962.

KÖRNER, S., *Kant*, Harmondsworth: Penguin, 1960.

PATON, H. J., *Kant's Metaphysic of Experience* (1936), 2 vols., New York: Macmillan, 1961.

PRICHARD, H. A., *Kant's Theory of Knowledge*, Oxford: Clarendon Press, 1909.

SMITH, N. K., *A Commentary to Kant's 'Critique of Pure Reason'*, 2nd edn. (1923), New York: Humanities Press, 1962.

STRAWSON, P., *The Bounds of Sense: An Essay on Kant's 'Critique of Pure Reason'*, London: Methuen, 1966.

BUCHDAHL, G., 'Causality, Causal Laws and Scientific Theory in the Philosophy of Kant', *Brit. J. Phil. Sci.* 16 (1965-6), 187-208.

BUCHDAHL, G., 'The Kantian "Dynamic of Reason", with Special Reference to the Place of Causality in Kant's System', in *Kant Studies Today*, ed. by L. W. Beck, La Salle: Open Court, 1969, 341-74.

9. *Analyses of the Implications of the New Science for a Theory of Scientific Method*
II. Theories of Scientific Procedure

WORKS BY HERSCHEL

A Preliminary Discourse on the Study of Natural Philosophy, London: Longman, Rees, Orme, Brown & Green and John Taylor, 1830.

Outlines of Astronomy, 2 vols., New York: P. F. Collier & Son, 1902.
Familiar Lectures on Scientific Subjects, New York: George Routledge and Sons, 1871.

WORKS ABOUT HERSCHEL

DUCASSE, C. J., 'John F. W. Herschel's Methods of Experimental Inquiry' in R. M. Blake, C. J. Ducasse, and E. H. Madden, *Theories of Scientific Method: The Renaissance Through the Nineteenth Century*, 153–82.
CANNON, W. F., 'John Herschel and the Idea of Science', *J. Hist. Ideas*, 22 (1961), 215–39.

WORKS BY WHEWELL

The Historical and Philosophical Works of William Whewell, ed. by G. Buchdahl and L. Laudan, London: Frank Cass, 1967–.
Astronomy and General Physics Considered with Reference to Natural Theology, Philadelphia, Pa.: Carey, Lea & Blanchard, 1836.
History of the Inductive Sciences (1837), 3 vols., New York: D. Appleton and Co., 1859.
The Philosophy of the Inductive Sciences, 2nd edn., 2 vols., London: J. W. Parker, 1847. 3rd edn. expanded into three parts: *The History of Scientific Ideas* (2 vols.), London: J. W. Parker and Son, 1858; *Novum Organon Renovatum*, 3rd edn., London: J. W. Parker and Son, 1858; and *On the Philosophy of Discovery*, London: J. W. Parker and Son, 1860.
William Whewell's Theory of Scientific Method, ed. by R. E. Butts, Pittsburgh, Pa.: University of Pittsburgh Press, 1968. Contains selections from Whewell's writings, a bibliography of works by and about Whewell, and an introductory essay by Butts.

WORKS ABOUT WHEWELL

BUTTS, R. E., 'Necessary Truth in Whewell's Philosophy of Science', *Am. Phil. Quart.* 2 (1965), 161–81.
BUTTS, R. E., 'On Walsh's Reading of Whewell's View of Necessity', *Phil. Sci.* 32 (1965), 175–81.
DUCASSE, C. J., 'Whewell's Philosophy of Scientific Discovery', *Phil. Rev.*, 60 (1951), 56–69; 213–34. Reprinted in R. M. Blake, C. J. Ducasse, and E. H. Madden, *Theories of Scientific Method: The Renaissance Through the Nineteenth Century*, Chap. 9.
HEATHCOTE, A. W., 'William Whewell's Philosophy of Science', *Brit. J. Phil. Sci.*, 4 (1953–4), 302–14.
STRONG, E. W., 'William Whewell and John Stuart Mill: Their Controversy About Scientific Knowledge', *J. Hist. Ideas*, 16 (1955), 209–31.
WALSH, H. T., 'Whewell and Mill on Induction', *Phil. Sci.* 29 (1962), 279–84.
WALSH, H. T., 'Whewell on Necessity', *Phil. Sci.* 29 (1962), 139–45.

WORKS BY MEYERSON

Du cheminement de la pensée, 3 vols., Paris: F. Alcan, 1931.
La déduction rélativiste, Paris: Payot, 1925.
De l'explication dans les sciences, Paris: Payot, 1927.
Identity and Reality (1908), trans. by K. Loewenberg, New York: Dover Publications, 1962.
Réel et determinisme dans la physique quantique, Paris: Hermann, 1933.

WORKS ABOUT MEYERSON

BOAS, G. A., *A Critical Analysis of the Philosophy of Émile Meyerson*, Baltimore. Md.: Johns Hopkins Press, 1930.
KELLY, T. R., *Explanation and Reality in the Philosophy of Émile Meyerson*, Princeton, N.J.: Princeton University Press, 1937.
LALUMIA, J., *The Ways of Reason. A Critical Study of the Ideas of Émile Meyerson*, New York: Humanities Press, 1966.
HILLMAN, O. N., 'Émile Meyerson on Scientific Explanation', *Phil. Sci.* 5 (1938), 73–80.

9. *Analysis of the Implications of the New Science for a Theory of Scientific Method*
III. Structure of Scientific Theories

WORKS BY DUHEM

The Aim and Structure of Physical Theory (2nd edn., 1914), trans. by P. P. Wiener, New York: Atheneum, 1962.
Études sur Léonard de Vinci. 3 vols, Paris: A. Hermann, 1906–13.
Le système du monde. Histoire des doctrines cosmologiques de Platon à Copernic. 5 vols, Paris: A. Hermann et fils, 1913–17. Reissued, 6 vols., 1954.
To Save the Phenomena, trans. by E. Doland and C. Maschler, Chicago, Ill.: University of Chicago Press, 1969.

WORKS ABOUT DUHEM

LOWINGER, A., *The Methodology of Pierre Duhem*, New York: Columbia University Press, 1941.
AGASSI, J., 'Duhem versus Galileo', *Brit. J. Phil. Sci.* 8 (1957–8), 237–48.
ALEXANDER, P., 'The Philosophy of Science, 1850–1910' in *A Critical History of Western Philosophy*, ed. by D. J. O'Connor, New York: Free Press, 1964, 417–20.
GINZBURG, B., 'Duhem and Jordanus Nemorarius', *Isis*, 25 (1936), 341–62.

WORKS BY CAMPBELL

Foundations of Science (formerly, *Physics: The Elements*, 1919), New York: Dover Publications, 1957.
What is Science? (1921), New York: Dover Publications, 1952.

WORKS ABOUT CAMPBELL

HEMPEL, C. G., *Aspects of Scientific Explanation and Other Essays in the Philosophy of Science*, New York: Free Press, 1965, 206–10; 442–7.

HESSE, M. B., *Models and Analogies in Science*, New York: Sheed & Ward, 1963 (*passim*).

SCHLESINGER, G., *Method in the Physical Sciences*, New York: Humanities Press, 1963. Chap. 3, sec. 5.

WORKS BY HEMPEL

Aspects of Scientific Explanation and Other Essays in the Philosophy of Science, New York: Free Press, 1965.

Philosophy of Natural Science, Englewood Cliffs, N.J.: Prentice-Hall, 1966.

'Deductive-Nomological vs. Statistical Explanation', in *Minnesota Studies in the Philosophy of Science*, vol. 3, ed. by H. Feigl and G. Maxwell, Minneapolis: University of Minnesota Press, 1962, 98–169.

'Fundamentals of Concept Formation in Empirical Science', *International Encyclopedia of Unified Science*, vol. II, No. 7, Chicago, Ill.: University of Chicago Press, 1952.

'Geometry and Empirical Science', *Amer. Math. Monthly* 52 (1945), 7–17. Reprinted in *Readings in Philosophical Analysis*, ed. by H. Feigl and W. Sellars, 238–49.

'On the Nature of Mathematical Truth', *Amer. Math. Monthly*, 52 (1945), 543–56. Reprinted in *Readings in Philosophical Analysis*, ed. by H. Feigl and W. Sellars, 222–37. Reprinted also in *Readings in the Philosophy of Science*, ed. by H. Feigl and M. Brodbeck, 148–62.

WORKS ABOUT HEMPEL

CARNAP, R., *Logical Foundations of Probability*, Chicago, Ill.: University of Chicago Press, 1950, secs. 87, 88.

SCHEFFLER, I., *The Anatomy of Inquiry*, New York: Alfred A. Knopf, 1963. Part III contains a discussion of Hempel's view of confirmation.

WORKS BY HESSE

Forces and Fields, London: Nelson, 1961.

Models and Analogies in Science, Notre Dame, Ind.: University of Notre Dame Press, 1966.

Science and the Human Imagination, London: S.C.M. Press, 1954.

'An Inductive Logic of Theories', in *Minnesota Studies in the Philosophy of Science*, ed. by M. Radner and S. Winokur, Minneapolis: University of Minnesota Press, 1970, 164–80.

'Analogy and Confirmation Theory', *Phil. Sci.* 31 (1964), 319–27.

'Consilience of Inductions', in *The Problem of Inductive Logic*, ed. by I. Lakatos, Amsterdam: North Holland Publishing Co., 1968, 232–46; 254–7.

'Is There an Independent Observation Language?', in *The Nature and Function of Scientific Theories*, ed. by R. Colodny, Pittsburgh, Pa.: University of Pittsburgh Press, 1970, 35–77.

'Models in Physics', *Brit. J. Phil. Sci.* 4 (1953–4), 198–214.

'Positivism and the Logic of Scientific Theories', in *The Legacy of Logical Positivism*, ed. by P. Achinstein and S. Barker, Baltimore: Johns Hopkins Press, 1969, 85–114.

'Theories, Dictionaries, and Observation', *Brit. J. Phil. Sci.* 9 (1958–9), 12–28.

WORKS BY HARRÉ

The Anticipation of Nature. London: Hutchinson, 1965.

The Explanation of Social Behaviour, with Paul Secord. Oxford: Basil Blackwell, in press.

An Introduction to the Logic of the Sciences, London: Macmillan, 1967.

Matter and Method, London: Macmillan, 1964.

The Method of Science, London: Wykeham Publications, 1970.

Philosophies of Science, Oxford: Oxford University Press, 1972.

The Principles of Scientific Thinking, London: Macmillan, 1970.

Theories and Things, London: Newman History and Philosophy of Science Series, 1961.

'Concepts and Criteria', *Mind*, 73 (1964), 353–63.

'Powers', *Brit. J. Phil. Sci.* 21, no. 1 (February 1970), 81–101.

10. Inductivism v. the Hypothetico-Deductive View of Science

WORKS BY MILL

Works, ed. by F. E. L. Priestley, J. M. Robson, *et al.* Toronto, Ont.: University of Toronto Press, 1963–.

A System of Logic: Ratiocinative and Inductive, 6th edn., London: Longmans, Green, 1865.

WORKS ABOUT MILL

ANSCHUTZ, R. P., *The Philosophy of J. S. Mill*, Oxford: Clarendon Press, 1953.

BRADLEY, F. H., *Principles of Logic*, 2nd edn., Oxford: Oxford University Press, 1928. Bk. 2, part II, chap. 3 includes a discussion of Mill's view of induction.

DUCASSE, C. J., 'John Stuart Mill's System of Logic', in R. M. Blake, C. J. Ducasse, and E. H. Madden, *Theories of Scientific Method: The Renaissance through the Nineteenth Century*, 218–32.

JEVONS, W. S., 'John Stuart Mill's Philosophy Tested', Part 2 of *Pure Logic and Other Minor Works*, London: Macmillan, 1890.

RYAN, A., *The Philosophy of John Stuart Mill*, London: Macmillan, 1970.

WORKS BY NAGEL

Logic Without Metaphysics, and Other Essays in the Philosophy of Science, Glencoe:
    Free Press, 1956.
Sovereign Reason and Other Studies in the Philosophy of Science, Glencoe: Free
    Press, 1954.
The Structure of Science, New York: Harcourt, Brace & World, 1961.
'Principles of the Theory of Probability', in *The International Encyclopedia of
    Unified Science,* vol. I, no. 6. Chicago, Ill.: University of Chicago Press,
    1939.
An Introduction to Logic and Scientific Method, with M. R. Cohen, New York:
    Harcourt, Brace, 1934.

WORKS BY FRANK

A Bibliography of Philipp Frank. Selected Writings on the Philosophy of Science. In
    R. S. Cohen and M. W. Wartofsky, eds. *Boston Studies in the Philosophy
    of Science,* vol. II, New York: Humanities Press, 1965, xxxi–xxxiv.
Modern Science and Its Philosophy, New York: George Braziller, 1955.
Philosophy of Science, Englewood Cliffs, N.J.: Prentice-Hall, 1957.
'Einstein, Mach, and Logical Positivism', in *Albert Einstein: Philosopher-
    Scientist,* ed. by P. A. Schilp, New York: Tudor Publishing Company,
    1951, 271–86.
'Foundations of Physics', in *International Encyclopedia of Unified Science,* ed. by
    O. Neurath, R. Carnap, and C. Morris (combined edition vol. I, nos.
    6–10), Chicago, Ill.: University of Chicago Press, 1955, 424–504.
'Metaphysical Interpretations of Science', *Brit. J. Phil. Sci.* I (1950–1),
    60–91.
'The Variety of Reasons for the Acceptance of Scientific Theories', in *The
    Validation of Scientific Theories,* ed. by P. Frank, Boston: Beacon Press,
    1954.

11. *Mathematical Positivism and Conventionalism*

WORKS BY BERKELEY

The Works of George Berkeley, Bishop of Cloyne. 9 vols., ed. by A. A. Luce and
    T. E. Jessop, London: Thomas Nelson and Sons, 1948–57.

WORKS ABOUT BERKELEY

LUCE, A. A., *The Dialectic of Immaterialism,* London: Hodder and Stoughton,
    1963.
WILD, J., *George Berkeley; A Study of His Life and Philosophy,* New York:
    Russell & Russell, 1962.
MYHILL, J., 'Berkeley's *De Motu*—An Anticipation of Mach', in *George
    Berkeley: Lectures Delivered Before the Philosophical Union of the University
    of California,* Berkeley: University of California Press, 1957, 141–57.

POPPER, K. R., 'A Note on Berkeley as Precursor of Mach', *Brit. J. Phil. Sci.* 4 (1953–54), 26–36.
WHITROW, G. J., 'Berkeley's Philosophy of Motion', *Brit. J. Phil. Sci.* 4 (1953–54), 37–45.

WORKS BY MACH

The Analysis of Sensations (1886), trans. by C. M. Williams, New York: Dover Publications, 1959.
History and Root of the Principle of the Conservation of Energy (1872), trans. by P. E. Jourdain, Chicago, Ill.: Open Court Publishing Co., 1910.
Popular Scientific Lectures (1896), trans. by T. J. McCormack, Chicago, Ill.: Open Court Publishing Co., 1943.
The Science of Mechanics (1883), trans. by T. J. McCormack, La Salle, Ill.: Open Court Publishing Co., 1960.
Space and Geometry (1901–3), trans. by T. J. McCormack, Chicago, Ill.: Open Court Publishing Co., 1906.

WORKS ABOUT MACH

COHEN, R. S. and SEEGER, R. J., eds. *Ernst Mach, Physicist and Philosopher* (Boston Studies in the Philosophy of Science, vol. VI), New York: Humanities Press, 1970. Contains a bibliography of works by and about Mach.
FRANK, P., *Modern Science and Its Philosophy*, chaps. 2, 3, New York: George Braziller, 1961, 13–62; 69–95.
ALEXANDER, P. 'The Philosophy of Science, 1850–1910', in *A Critical History of Western Philosophy*, ed. by D. J. O'Connor, New York: Free Press, 1964, 403–9.
BUNGE, M., 'Mach's Critique of Newtonian Mechanics', *Am. J. Phys.* 34 (1966), 585–96.

WORKS BY POINCARÉ

Mathematics and Science: Last Essays (English translation by J. W. Bolduc of *Dernières Pensées*, 1913), New York: Dover Publications, 1963.
Science and Hypothesis (1902), trans. by G. B. Halsted, New York: Science Press, 1905.
Science and Method (1909), trans. by F. Maitland, New York: Dover Publications, 1952.
The Value of Science (1905), trans. by G. B. Halsted, New York: Science Press, 1907.

WORKS ABOUT POINCARÉ

ALEXANDER, P., 'The Philosophy of Science, 1850–1910', in *A Critical History of Western Philosophy*, ed. by D. J. O'Connor, New York: Free Press, 413–17.

WORKS BY HANSON

A Bibliography of Publications by N. R. Hanson is given in *Boston Studies in the Philosophy of Science*, vol. 3, Dordrecht: D. Reidel Publishing Company, 1967, xliii–xlix.

The Concept of the Positron, Cambridge: Cambridge University Press, 1963.

Patterns of Discovery, Cambridge: Cambridge University Press, 1958.

Perception and Discovery, ed. by W. C. Humphreys, San Francisco, Calif.: Freeman, Cooper, 1969.

'An Anatomy of Discovery', *J. Phil.* 64 (1967), 321–52.

'Copenhagen Interpretation of Quantum Theory', *Am. J. Phys.* 27 (1959), 1–15.

'Five Cautions for the Copenhagen Interpretation's Critics', *Phil. Sci.* 26 (1959), 325–37.

'The Irrelevance of History of Science to Philosophy of Science', *J. Phil.* 59 (1962), 574–86.

'The Logic of Discovery', *J. Phil.* 55 (1958), 1073–89.

'Newton's First Law: A Philosopher's Door into Natural Philosophy', in *Beyond the Edge of Certainty: Essays in Contemporary Science and Philosophy*, ed. by R. Colodny. Englewood Cliffs, N.J.: Prentice-Hall, 1965, 6–28.

12. *Twentieth-Century Views on the Demarcation of Science*

WORKS BY BRIDGMAN

Dimensional Analysis, New Haven, Conn.: Yale University Press, 1931.

The Logic of Modern Physics, New York: Macmillan, 1927.

The Nature of Physical Theory, Princeton, N.J.: Princeton University Press, 1936.

Reflections of a Physicist, New York: Philosophical Library, 1950.

A Sophisticate's Primer of Relativity, Middletown, Conn.: Wesleyan University Press, 1962.

The Way Things Are, Cambridge, Mass.: Harvard University Press, 1959.

'The Nature of Some of our Physical Concepts', *Brit. J. Phil. Sci.* 1 (1950–1), 257–72; 2 (1951–2), 25–44; 142–60.

WORKS ABOUT BRIDGMAN

BENJAMIN, A. C., *Operationalism*, Springfield, Ill.: Charles C. Thomas, 1955.

BERGMANN, G., 'Sense and Nonsense in Operationism', in *The Validation of Scientific Theories*, ed. by P. Frank, 41–52.

HEMPEL, C., 'A Logical Appraisal of Operationism', in *The Validation of Scientific Theories*, 52–67.

LINDSAY, R. B., 'A Critique of Operationalism in Physics', *Phil. Sci.* 4 (1937), 456–70.

MARGENAU, H., 'Interpretations and Misinterpretations of Operationalism', in *The Validation of Scientific Theories*, 39–40.

WORKS BY CARNAP

Logical Foundations of Probability, 2nd edn., Chicago, Ill.: University of Chicago Press, 1962.

The Logical Syntax of Language, trans. by A. Smeaton, London: Kegan Paul Trench, Trubner, 1937.

Meaning and Necessity, 2nd edn., Chicago, Ill.: University of Chicago Press, 1956.

Philosophical Foundations of Physics, ed. by M. Gardner, New York: Basic Books, 1966.

'The Elimination of Metaphysics through Logical Analysis of Language', trans. by A. Pap (1932), in *Logical Positivism*, ed. by A. J. Ayer, Glencoe: Free Press, 1959, 60–81.

'The Interpretation of Physics' (1939), in *Readings in the Philosophy of Science*, ed. by H. Feigl and M. Brodbeck, New York: Appleton-Century-Crofts, 309–18.

'Logical Foundations of the Unity of Science', in *International Encyclopedia of Unified Science*, ed. by O. Neurath, R. Carnap, and C. Morris (combined edition, vol. I, nos. 1–5), Chicago, Ill.: University of Chicago Press, 1955, 42–62.

'Psychology in Physical Language' (1931), trans. by G. Schick, in *Logical Positivism*, ed. A. J. Ayer, 165–98.

'Testability and Meaning', *Phil. Sci.* 3 (1936), 419–31, and 4 (1937), 1–40. Reprinted in *Readings in the Philosophy of Science*, ed. by H. Feigl and M. Brodbeck, 47–92.

'The Two Concepts of Probability', in *Readings in the Philosophy of Science*, ed. by H. Feigl and M. Brodbeck, 438–55.

WORKS ABOUT CARNAP

The Philosophy of Rudolf Carnap, ed. by P. A. Schilpp, La Salle: Open Court Publishing Co., 1963. Contains an 'Intellectual Autobiography' by Carnap, numerous essays on Carnap's philosophy, and a bibliography of Carnap's writings, compiled by A. J. Benson.

WORKS BY AYER

The Concept of a Person, New York: St. Martin's Press, 1963.

The Foundations of Empirical Knowledge, London: Macmillan, 1940.

Language, Truth and Logic, 2nd edn., revised (1946), New York: Dover Publications, 1952.

Philosophical Essays, New York: St. Martin's Press, 1954.

The Problem of Knowledge, New York: St. Martin's Press, 1956.

WORKS ABOUT AYER

Church, A., 'Review of A. J. Ayer, *Language, Truth and Logic*', *J. Symbol. Logic*, 14 (1949), 52–3.

LAZEROWITZ, M., 'Strong and Weak Verification I', *Mind*, 48 (1939), 202–13; 'Strong and Weak Verification II', *Mind*, 59 (1950), 345–57. Both reprinted in M. Lazerowitz, *The Structure of Metaphysics*, London: Routledge and Kegan Paul, 1955.

MAKINSON, D., 'Nidditch's Definition of Verifiability', *Mind*, 74 (1965), 240–7.

NIDDITCH, P., 'A Defense of Ayer's Verifiability Principle Against Church's Criticism', *Mind*, 70 (1961), 88–9.

WORKS BY POPPER

Conjectures and Refutations, New York: Basic Books, 1963.

The Logic of Scientific Discovery, New York: Basic Books, 1959 (1st edn., *Logik der Forschung*, 1934).

The Open Society and Its Enemies. 2 vols., 4th edn., revised, New York: Harper Torchbooks, 1963.

'The Demarcation Between Science and Metaphysics', in *The Philosophy of Rudolf Carnap*, ed. by P. A. Schilpp, La Salle: Open Court, 1963, 183–226.

'Indeterminism in Quantum Physics and in Classical Physics', *Brit. J. Phil. Sci.* 1 (1950–1), 117–33; 173–95.

'The Nature of Philosophical Problems and their Roots in Science', *Brit. J. Phil. Sci.* 3 (1952–3), 124–56.

'A Note on Natural Laws and So-Called "Contrary-to-Fact Conditionals" ', *Mind*, 58 (1949), 62–6.

'Philosophy of Science: A Personal Report', in C. A. Mace, *British Philosophy in the Mid-Century*, London: George Allen and Unwin, 1957, 155–91.

'The Propensity Interpretation of Probability', *Brit. J. Phil. Sci.* 10 (1959–60), 25–42.

WORKS ABOUT POPPER

BUNGE, M. A., ed., *The Critical Approach to Science and Philosophy*, Glencoe: Free Press, 1964. A collection of articles, with a bibliography of Popper's publications.

FAIN, H., 'Review of The Logic of Scientific Discovery', *Phil. Sci.* 28 (1961), 319–24.

LAKATOS, I. and MUSGRAVE, A., eds., *Criticism and the Growth of Knowledge*, Cambridge: Cambridge University Press, 1970. Contains essays on the views of scientific change of Popper and T. S. Kuhn.

SCHILPP, P. A., ed., *The Philosophy of Karl R. Popper*, La Salle: Open Court Publishing Co., forthcoming. A volume in the 'Library of Living Philosophers' series.

Index of Proper Names

Index of subjects